chemical analysis
by
emission spectroscopy

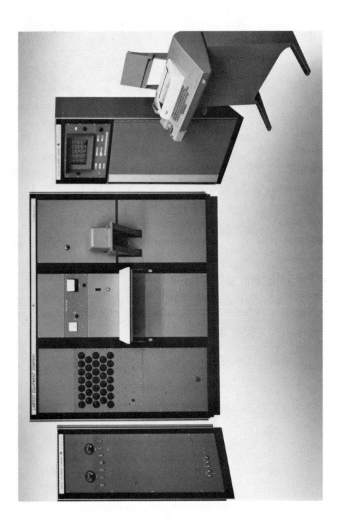

A modern automatic industrial spectrometer

This instrument is capable of quantitatively analyzing a metal sample for as many as fifty elements, simultaneously. The results, which are available in less than two minutes, are displayed on the face of a cathode-ray tube, similar to a TV screen, in the cabinet at the right. They can also be printed out on a teletypewriter which may be in the same room with the spectrometer, as shown, or at a remote location (Courtesy of Labtest Equipment Co., Los Angeles, California).

chemical analysis
by
emission spectroscopy

SAM EPSTEIN

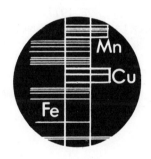

FRANKLIN publishing company, inc.
PALISADE, New Jersey 07024

© 1977
FRANKLIN PUBLISHING COMPANY, INC.
Palisade,   New Jersey 07024

Printed in the United States of America

Table of contents

Introduction

The spectroscope, whose development was based on Isaac Newton's experiments on the dispersion of sunlight by a glass prism, was the first of a long series of chemicoanalytical instruments that today sometimes are referred to as "black boxes" because their appearance, unlike that of flasks, beakers, and test tubes, gives no clue as to how they operate.

Reports on the discoveries of R. Bunsen and G. Kirchhoff in Germany during the 50's and 60's of the last century, which laid the foundations of spectrochemical analysis, were greeted by the public, both lay and scientific, with much the same kind of amazement and interest as was later generated by the discovery of Xrays and atomic energy. This is not surprising since the spectroscope, an instrument that detects the chemical elements present in a substance by the light it emits as it burns, enabled chemists to perform in just a few seconds analyses that required hours or days by conventional methods and even discover several new elements.

The power of the spectroscope was even more dramatically illustrated when it was added to the arsenal of instruments used by the astronomer. Of all the accepted ideas of the mid-19th-century, none was considered more immune to the steam-roller advance of science than the belief that knowledge of the composition of the heavenly bodies was forever beyond the grasp of man. Yet, analysis of light from the sun and stars soon showed that they are composed of many of the chemical elements found on earth. As a matter of fact, one element, helium, was detected in the sun *before* it was discovered on earth.

At the micro end of the scale of matter, our present picture of the atom with its nucleus and orbiting electrons is due to the Danish physicist, Niels Bohr, winner of the Nobel prize, who based his theory to a large extent on spectroscopic information.

On the more practical side, the spectroscope is a key instrument in modern science and technology. It is used for the analysis of metallic elements in such variety of materials as minerals, metallurgical and petroleum

6

products, biological substances, and high-purity electronic components, as well as in the fields of crime detection and environmental-pollution control. An especially interesting job for the spectroscope is the analysis of moon rocks. In the aluminum and steel industries, automatic spectroscopes provide the almost instantaneous analysis of samples that is required to keep their furnaces operating at top efficiency.

In recent years, many competing systems of instrumental analysis have been developed, none of which has the basic simplicity, analytical comprehensiveness, and low cost that make possible the meaningful use of the spectroscope for researchers, students, science amateurs, industrial operations, rock hounds, and many others.

This book presents the basic theory required to understand the construction and operation of spectroscopes and spectrographs. Instruments in the $200 to $15,000 range that are representative of those currently being manufactured are discussed and their application to the qualitative and quantitative analysis of many types of substances is explained.

For those interested in building their own spectrograph, either by necessity or by choice, the design and construction of an easy-to-build, inexpensive, reliable instrument that can be used in countless analytical applications is described.

The author's qualifications for writing this book include many years of experience as a chemist and spectroscopist in the field of metal analysis and working for a manufacturer of direct-reading industrial spectrometers.

CHAPTER 1

The historical background of spectroscopy

The *spectrum,* the array of colors that is produced when sunlight passes under certain conditions through a transparent substance, such as water or glass, has always been known to man in its most spectacular form, the rainbow. Its sudden appearance after a rainstorm as the sun emerges from behind the clouds is an awe-inspiring sight that, until relatively recent times, was attributed to supernatural causes and, as such, incorporated into religious beliefs. For example, in the Old Testament, Genesis: 9, the rainbow is explained as the symbol of a promise by God to Noah that never again would He subject the earth to another life-destroying flood.

The spectrum can be observed on a small scale when sunlight strikes a drop of water clinging to a leaf or when it passes through a transparent solid, such as a diamond. A similar phenomenon is seen when a source of light is viewed through fabric of closely woven fine threads.

Spectroscopy, the scientific study of the spectrum, was born in 1666 when Isaac Newton discovered how a *prism,* a piece of glass of triangular cross section, separates white light into its component colors. In a darkened room, he allowed a beam of sunlight from a small opening in a window shutter to pass through a prism as shown in Figure 1-1 and observed the resulting spectrum on the opposite wall.

Newton distinguished seven colors: red, orange, yellow, green, blue, indigo, and violet. There are no sharp boundries but rather a gradual change from one color to the next. By masking all except a narrow band of color and allowing it to pass through a second prism he satisfied himself that there was no further separation into additional colors. In other words, within the limitations of his primitive apparatus, he had isolated what is today known as *monochromatic* light (light of one color). When he passed

8

the spectrum through a second prism that was upside down with respect to the first one, the colors were reunited and a spot of white light appeared on the wall.

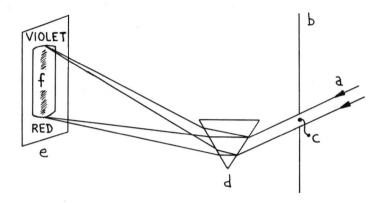

Figure 1—1 NEWTON'S EXPERIMENT
a — sunlight; *b* — window shutter; *c* — hole in shutter; *d* — glass prism; *e* — wall; *f* — spectrum.

In this way, Newton proved that white light is a mixture of the spectral colors. The prism separates the colors by bending, *refracting,* each through a different angle, violet through the largest and red through the smallest. The separation, *dispersion,* between any two parts of the spectrum depends on the chemical composition of the prism material.

In 1800, the English astronomer, William Herschel, discovered that a thermometer registered a constantly increasing temperature as it was moved toward the red end of the spectrum, an effect that continued into the invisible region that is now called the *infrared.* The human eye is insensitive to infrared radiation but it can be detected through the sensation of heat.

The German scientist, J. W. Ritter, discovered in 1801 that the spectrum also extends beyond the violet end. He observed that the degree of darkening of a silver chloride-coated paper (actually a crude photographic film) was greatest when exposed to violet light. The paper was even more strongly affected in the invisible *ultraviolet* region.

William Wollaston, an English chemist, repeated Newton's experiment in 1802 and observed that the spectrum of sunlight entering through a narrow crack is not continuous but is interrupted by many black lines each being an image of the crack. He also examined the spectrum of candlelight passed through a narrow slit and found it to be composed of several broad bands of color and a yellow line. Although Wollaston did not realize it, his experiments contained the first hints of the powerful scientific tool that spectroscopy was to become. Our present knowledge of both the structure of the universe and the atom depends largely on spectroscopic information. Many chemical elements have been discovered by spectroscopic methods and spectrochemical analytical instruments are indispensible to modern technology.

In 1817, Joseph von Fraunhofer, a German optician and physicist, reported the results of a careful study of the dark lines in the sun's spectrum that he had made with a device of his own design that was very much like a modern *spectroscope,* an instrument for producing and viewing spectra. The basic features of Fraunhofer's spectroscope are shown *in Figure 1-2.*

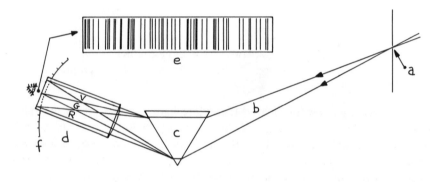

Figure 1–2 FRAUNHOFER'S SPECTROSCOPE

a — slit; *b* — light after passing through slit; *c* — prism; *d* — telescope tube; *e* — spectral lines as seen in the telescope; *f* — reference scale; *V, G, R,* — violet, green, red.

He labeled the most prominent lines A, B, C, etc., a notation that is still in use today. His "D" line coincided exactly with the yellow line that Wollaston had detected in a candle flame. The dark lines were named Fraunhofer lines in his honor but it remained for a later investigator to discover their significance.

With his instrument, Fraunhofer was able to measure the position of a spectral line with respect to other lines rather than describing it simply as yellow or blue or whatever its color. He rotated telescope tube *d* with respect to prism *c* until the line in question was centered in the field of view and noted the position of the tube on scale *f.*

By 1860, the Fraunhofer lines had been explained, the modern form of the spectroscope had evolved, and the foundations of analytical spectrochemistry had been laid. Foremost among those who contributed to the solution of these problems were physicist Gustav Kirchhoff and chemist Robert Bunsen, both Germans. Figure 1-3 is an engraving of the type of instrument that was used by the two collaborators. It is an improved form of Fraunhofer's spectroscope. The slit, not visible, is at the end of tube *A* in which is also mounted a *collimating* lens that sends parallel lightrays into prism *P*. Light from a source (not shown) passes through opening *S* and illuminates a reference scale inside tube *C*. An image of the scale appears in the field of view of telescope tube *B* above the spectrum and is used for line identification.

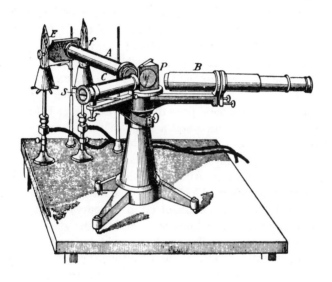

Figure 1–3 BUNSEN-KIRCHHOFF SPECTROSCOPE
A — collimator tube; *B* — telescope tube; *C* — reference-scale tube; *E* — sample-excitation source (gas flame); *f* — reference-sample-excitation source (gas flame); *P* — prism; *S* — opening for the reference-scale illuminating light.

For many years, it had been known but not generally accepted that the bright lines in the spectra of metals, vaporized in a flame or by an electric spark, could be used for chemical analysis. Bunsen and Kirchhoff proved conclusively that the atoms of a vaporized metal emit light that appears in the spectroscope in the form of characteristic lines which positively identify the metal. For example, the yellow D line (actually two closely spaced lines) always appears at exactly the same position in the spectrum of any substance that contains sodium. Four specific red lines can be seen in the spectrum of potassium-bearing substances. Lithium and strontium also emit red lines which are, however, distinguishable from each other as well as from those of potassium. Green lines are associated with barium, etc.

The elements of the alkali-metal and alkaline-earth group were used by Bunsen and Kirchhoff in their researches because they emit their characteristic spectra at the relatively low temperature of a bunsen-burner flame which was the most efficient and convenient heat source available at that time. Most of the other metals must be vaporized in hotter flames or in an electric arc to excite their spectra but the principle involved is the same.

With their newly developed technique, Bunsen and Kirchhoff were able to perform analyses in much less time and detect far smaller con-centrations of metals than was possible by conventional wet chemical methods. The power of spectrochemical analysis was further demonstrated when they announced the discovery of two new elements, cesium and rubidium, on the basis of several blue and red lines which appeared in the spectrum of a mineral specimen, lines that they had never before observed. These metals were soon isolated and a study of their chemical and physi-cal properties showed them to be members of the alkali group.

Kirchhoff solved the mystery of the dark lines in the sun's spectrum with the following experiment. After observing the yellow sodium doublet in a flame containing sodium chloride, he placed a glass plate coated with sodium amalgam (sodium metal dissolved in mercury) between the flame and the spectroscope slit but below them. Heating the glass with a second burner, he vaporized some of the amalgam and produced a cloud of rel-atively cool, nonemitting sodium atoms through which the light from the first burner had to pass before entering the spectroscope. Under these conditions, two black lines appeared in place of the yellow ones. Kirchhoff was able to produce dark-line spectra of other elements also.

This experiment proves that atoms in the vapor state but below their emitting temperature absorb light of the same wavelength as they can emit. This provides an explanation for the presence of Fraunhofer lines in the solar spectrum. The incandescent surface of the sun emits a *continuous* (complete) spectrum. Its *photosphere,* which corresponds to the earth's atmosphere, consists of atoms of many different elements each of which absorbs from the sun's light those wavelengths they would emit at higher temperatures. The composition of the photosphere can be deter-mined by matching dark lines in the solar spectrum with corresponding bright lines of chemical elements on earth. Sixty six elements have been identified in the sun, including helium whose lines were detected in the solar spectrum before it was discovered on earth.

Advances in photography made possible the development of the *spectrograph,* a modified spectroscope in which a camera replaces the eyepiece. A *spectrogram,* a picture of a spectrum, is a permanent record that can be studied at leisure in contrast to the immediate and usually short examination that must be made with a spectroscope. In addition, the spectrograph records regions of the spectrum that cannot be detected by the human eye.

What is light? Newton and his followers believed that it consisted of a stream of small particles which they called corpuscles but they were unable to support their corpuscular theory by experimental evidence. On the other side were the advocates of the wave theory. The most influential among them was the Dutch physicist, Christian Huyghens. They argued that light is transmitted in the form of three-dimensional, spherical waves similar to the two-dimensional, circular waves that are formed when the surface of a liquid is disturbed.

In 1802, Thomas Young reported to the Royal Society of London the results of his famous two-slit experiment by which he succeeded in detecting *interference* effects with light (alternate light and dark fringes on a screen) which is to be expected from the wave theory. In 1826, his ideas were extended and clarified by the French physicist, Augustin Fresnel, in a paper on the *diffraction* of light which explains how interference results in the formation of spectra. Young's experiment shows the wavelength of red light to be approximately 0.00007 centimeter, that of green light 0.00005 centimeter, and that of violet light 0.00004 centimeter.

Fraunhofer constructed a device called a *diffraction grating* which consisted of fine silver wire wound around a frame to form many closely spaced, narrow openings. With his grating he was able to produce spectra of much greater dispersion and intensity than was possible with a double slit. In 1823, he ruled 4000 grooves with a diamond point on an area 1/2-inch wide on a piece of flat glass. This is the modern form of the *plane transmission* grating. By applying Young's principle, Fraunhofer was able to measure the wavelengths of many of the solar dark lines with his grating. His results differ from the presently accepted ones by less than 1%. For example, his value for the wavelength of the D line was 0.00005886 centimeter compared to the presently accepted figure of 0.00005893

In 1869, the Swedish physicist, A. J. Angstrom, published the results of new measurements, made with the best gratings available, of the wavelengths of about one thousand of the most important spectral lines. In recognition of his work, the lengths of light waves are expressed in *angstrom* units (A). One angstrom corresponds to 10^{-8} centimeter. The average wavelength of the sodium doublet, for example, is 5893 A.

One of the most important contributions to spectroscopy was the invention of the *concave reflection grating* by H. A. Rowland, an American physicist, in 1880. Its grooves are ruled on the surface of a concave mirror with a machine called a ruling engine. The slit, grating, and camera of a concave-grating spectrograph are all located on a circle called the *Rowland circle.*

In 1913, the theoretical physicist, Niels Bohr of Denmark, proposed the currently accepted basic structure of the atom with its positively charged nucleus surrounded by orbiting electrons. He was awarded the Nobel prize for this discovery. When an atom is subjected to heat or an electrical discharge, one or more of it electrons may absorb energy and move into new orbits. In returning to their original state, the electrons emit the absorbed energy in the form of light of definite wavelengths. The wavelengths of hundreds of thousands of spectral lines have been measured and in compliance with the atomic theory, no two elements have even one line in common although many are so close together that only an extremely powerful spectrograph can separate them.

The bright future of the spectroscope as a new tool for the analytical chemist that seemed just over the horizon after the discoveries of Bunsen and Kirchhoff did not materialize until about seventy years later. Among the obstacles in the way of the advance of spectrochemistry were the low state of development of photography and electrical sources for vaporizing samples, the unavailability of extensive spectral-line tables and auxiliary equipment needed for the identification of unknown lines, and the lack of reliable methods for obtaining quantitative results. Since about 1930, however, progress has been rapid and today emission spectrocopy is a widely used technique for the detection and quantitative determination of metals at all concentration levels in almost any type of substance.

REFERENCES

(1)   *Encyclopedia of Spectroscopy,* edited by G. L. Clark, Reinhold Publishing Co., New York City (1960).

(2)   *Great Experiments in Physics,* edited by M. H. Shamos, Holt, Rinehart & Winston, New York City (1959). Page 93: The interference of light (Thomas Young); page 108: The diffraction of light (Augustin Fresnel); page 329: The hydrogen atom (Niels Bohr).

(3)   *Nineteenth Century Spectroscopy.* "Development of the Understanding of Spectra, 1802-1897," W. McGucken, Johns Hopkins Press, Baltimore, Md. (1969).

CHAPTER 2

The formation of spectra by prisms and diffraction gratings

The surfaces and dimensions of a prism are shown in Figure 2-1. A *principle section* is any plane through a prism parallel to its top. As light passes from one medium to another of greater density, its velocity is reduced by an amount that varies with the wavelength. This accounts for the refraction and dispersion of light by a prism.

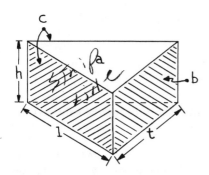

Figure 2-1. PRISM SURFACES AND DIMENSIONS
a — top; b — base; c — faces; h — height; l — length; t — thickness.

Let us assume that ray a in Figure 2-2 is a mixture of three wavelengths, λ_1, λ_2 and λ_3. As a enters the prism, each wavelength is refracted through a different angle. Refraction occurs again at the glass-air exit interface as the light leaves the prism, this time in the opposite direction, because the density of air is less than that of glass.

Figure 2-3 shows the refraction of a monochromatic ray. According to Snell's law (equation 2-1) the *index of refraction n is* constant for a given wavelength.

15

$$n = \sin i / \sin r \qquad \text{(Equation 2-1)}$$

Angle of incidence i and *angle of refraction r* are measured with respect to
p, the normal (perpendicular) to the prism face.

Ray *a* is shown passing through the prism symmetrically, that is, $i = i'$
and r=r'. Under these conditions, which are most favorable to the
formation of spectral lines, angle *d*, the over-all deviation of a ray, is at its
smallest possible value and the prism is said to be at *minimum deviation*.
In the case of an equilateral (60°) prism, the type most commonly used in
spectroscopes, angle *r* is always 30° at minimum deviation. Since sin 30°
is 0.5, equation 2-1 is simplified to

$$\sin i = 0.5n \qquad \text{(Equation 2-2)}$$

which allows calculation of the angle of incidence at minimum deviation for
any wavelength for which the index of refraction is known.

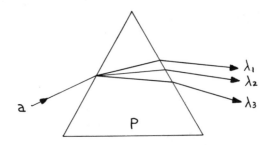

Figure 2-2. REFRACTION AND DISPERSION OF LIGHT BY A PRISM
a — entering light ray that is refracted by prism *P* and dispersed into its component
wavelengths λ_1, λ_2 and λ_3 .

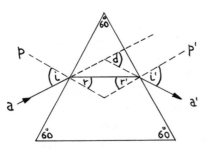

Figure 2-3. PATH OF A MONO-
CHROMATIC RAY THROUGH A
PRINCIPLE SECTION OF AN EQUI-
LATERAL PRISM AT MINIMUM
DEVIATION

p — normal to the prism entrance
face; *p'* — normal to the prism exit
face; *a* — entrance ray; *a'* — exit ray;
i — incident angle of the entrance
ray; *i'* — incident angle of the exit
ray; *r* — angle of refraction of the
entrance ray; *r'* — angle of refraction
of the exit ray; *d* — angle of deviation of the entrance ray.

Table 2-1 lists the indices of refraction for a number of common prism materials. Glass is used for visible wavelengths and quartz for ultraviolet. Salt prisms are required for infrared work because of their transparency in that region of the spectrum.

TABLE 2-1

Indices of refraction for some common prism materials at 5893 A

Material	n_D
Dense flint glass	1.656
Light flint glass	1.580
Silicate crown glass	1.527
Rock salt (NaCl)	1.544
Quartz (SiO₂)	1.458
Water *	1.333
Ethyl Cinnamate *	1.560
Air **	1.00029

*Glass-walled liquid-filled prisms are sometimes used in spectroscopes.
**Listed for comparison.

Subscript D of n indicates the wavelength for which the data in Table 2-1 apply.

Table 2-2 shows how the index of refraction typically varies with wavelength and the angle of incidence at minimum deviation for several wavelengths.

TABLE 2-2

Indices of refraction and minimum deviation angles for a 60° dense flint-glass prism for several wavelengths

n	Angle of incidence for mini- mum deviation (degrees)	Fraunhofer line designation	Wavelength (A)
1.644	55.2	C	6563
1.650	55.6	D	5893
1.665	56.3	F	4861
1.675	56.9	G'	4340

Prismatic spectra are said to be irrational because of the nonlinear relationship between index of refraction and wavelength, as shown in Figure 2-4.

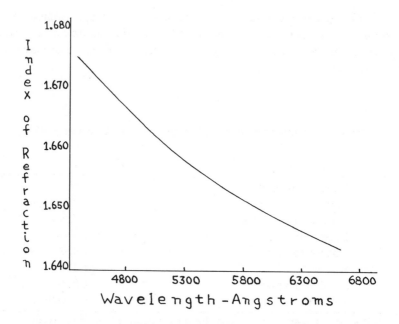

Figure 2-4. GRAPH OF THE INDEX OF REFRACTION VERSUS WAVELENGTH FOR THE DATA IN TABLE 2-2

The angular separation $\triangle \theta$ between any two rays for which the indices of refraction are known can be calculated from equation 2-3 which applies to equilateral prisms only.

$$\triangle \cdot \theta = 57.3\ (n_1 - n_2)/\sqrt{1 - \bar{n}^2/4}\ \text{degrees} \qquad \text{(Equation 2–3)}$$

The average value of indices n_1 and n_2 is designated by n.

For the prism in Table 2-2, the calculation for the angular separation or dispersion between the G' and C lines is as follows:

$$\triangle \theta = 57.3\ (1.675 - 1.644)/\sqrt{1 - (1.659)^2/4} = 5.69°$$

For the performance of a spectroscope, its *resolving power,* the ability to separate adjacent spectral lines, is just as important as its dispersion. Resolving power R is defined as

$$R = \lambda/\triangle\lambda \qquad \text{(Equation 2-4)}$$

λ being the average wavelength of the two lines to be resolved and $\triangle \lambda$ the difference in their wavelengths.

A common standard of resolving power, although not a particularly high one, is that required to separate the sodium D lines at 5890 A and 5896 A. Applying equation 2-4, we have

$$R = 5893/(5896 - 5890) = 982$$

The essential components of a prism spectroscope are shown in Figure 2-5. Collimator lens C throws parallel light from slit S onto prism P and telescope lens T focusses the resulting spectrum at eyepiece E for viewing (or on a film in a spectrograph).

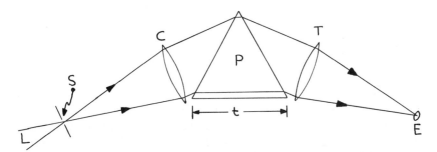

Figure 2-5. BASIC COMPONENTS OF A PRISM SPECTROSCOPE

L — light from excitation source; S — slit; C — collimator lens; P — prism; T — telescope lens; E — eyepiece; t — prism-base thickness (The light must completely fill the entrance face of the prism to take advantage of the full prism thickness. As shown, light L does not completely fill the prism face.)

Assuming a perfect optical system, which has an infinitely narrow slit, the resolving power is a function only of the prism-base thickness t and $dn/d\lambda$ the slope of the index *vs* wavelength curve (Figure 2-4) at the wavelength in question.

$$R = t \, (dn/d\lambda) \qquad \text{(Equation 2-5)}$$

However, there is no such thing as a perfect optical system. In practice, the slit must have a finite width so that light can enter the spectroscope and imperfections, such as component misalignment, lens aberrations, and prism defects all contribute to resolution loss. Nevertheless, the resolving power of a well-designed and well-constructed instrument may closely approach the theoretical value.

The dispersion of a spectroscope may be expressed as *angular dispersion* (equation 2-3) or as *linear dispersion*. The latter gives wavelength separation in terms of spectrum length, usually as millimeters per angstrom. Its inverse, *reciprocal linear dispersion,* angstroms per milli-meter, is more practical to measure. The dispersion of a prism spectroscope or spectrograph, and also of a plane-diffraction-grating instrument, is proportional to the focal length of its spectrum-focussing lens and, in the case of a concave-grating spectrograph, to the radius of the Rowland circle. In other words, a greater focal length produces a longer spectrum. The wavelength *vs* reciprocal dispersion relationship for a prism instrument enables the spectrographer to measure the wavelengths of and identify unknown spectral lines.

Common prism systems

(*1*) *Littrow prism* (Figure 2-6)

A Littrow half prism is equivalent to a full prism because of its reflecting surface *M,* which may be either silvered or aluminized. The high price of optical-quality quartz makes it an especially attractive prism for a quartz spectrograph. Reversal of the direction of the light by the mirror has the additional advantage of cancelling out the double refraction that occurs when light passes through natural quartz.

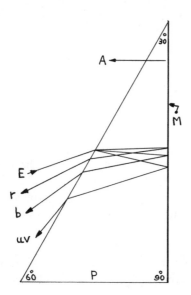

Figure 2-6. LITTROW-TYPE QUARTZ HALF-PRISM

A — crystal axis; *P* — quartz half-prism; *E* — entrance ray; *r* — red exit ray; *b* — blue exit ray; *uv* — ultra-violet exit ray; *M* — reflecting-mirror face.

(2) *Wadsworth prism* (Figure 2-7)

This is a *constant-deviation* arrangement, so called because minimum-deviation ray *g* is reflected by mirror *M* at a constant angle with respect to entrance ray *E*. Rotation of the prism-mirror system brings any desired wavelength to the minimum-deviation position and centers it in the field of view. This design allows the collimator and telescope tubes to be maintained in a fixed position parallel to each other when mirror *M* is in the position shown. Only one wavelength can be viewed at minimum deviation with the conventional Bunsen arrangement since the collimator tube and prism are fixed and the telescope tube must be rotated to scan the spectrum.

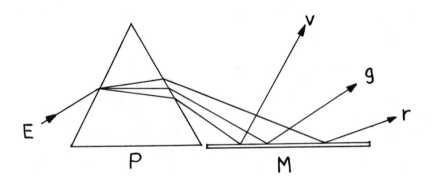

Figure 2-7. WADSWORTH-TYPE PRISM MOUNTING

E – entrance ray; *P* – equilateral prism; *M* – mirror; *r* – red exit ray; *g* – green exit ray (at minimum deviation); *v* – violet exit ray; rays *E* and *g* are parallel to each other.

(3) *Pellin-Broca prism* (Figure 2-8)

This is another constant-deviation design. Although the prism is a single piece of glass it is, as shown, in effect a three-prism system which maintains a constant angle of 90° between entering light *R-1* and emerging minimum-deviation ray *R-2*. This arrangement is very convenient for visual work.

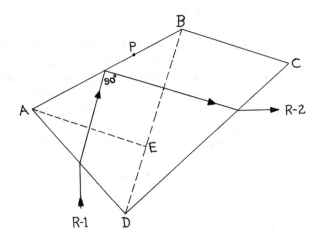

Figure 2-8. PELLIN-BROCA PRISM

ADE — 30° — 60° — 90° triangle; *ABE* — 45° — 45° — 90° triangle; *BCD* — 30° — 60° — 90° triangle; *P* — rotation point of prism (intersection of bisector of angle *ADC* and face *AB*); *R-1* — entrance ray; *R-2* — exit ray

(4) Amici direct-vision prism (Figure 2-9)

This is a compound prism made by cementing together three prisms made of different kinds of glass. The net effect is that light is dispersed but deviated only slightly from its original direction. Amici prisms, which have low dispersion and resolving power, are used in small hand-held spectroscopes for observing various types of spectra directly.

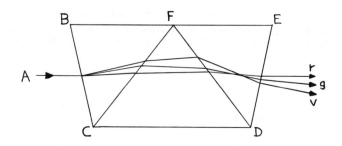

Figure 2-9. AMICI PRISM SYSTEM

BCF — crown-glass* prism; *DEF* — crown-glass* prism; *CDF* — flint-glass* prism; *A* — entrance ray; *r* — red exit ray; *g* — green exit ray; *v* — violet exit ray.

* Types of glass designed to have a specific index of refraction.

Diffraction gratings

A diffraction grating produces a spectrum because of the wave nature of light. A grating consists of a plane or a concave surface on which many shallow, closely spaced, equidistant grooves have been ruled. Depending on whether the light passes through or is reflected by the grating, it is called a transmission or reflection grating. Concave gratings are always of the reflection type.

The formation of a two-wavelength spectrum through the diffraction of light by a three-groove, plane reflection grating is shown schematically in Figure 2-10. Parallel light r strikes the grating at incident angle i. Each wavelength is diffracted by the grooves at a different angle with the formation of a spectrum which can be focussed, by an appropriately positioned lens, on a film or for direct viewing.

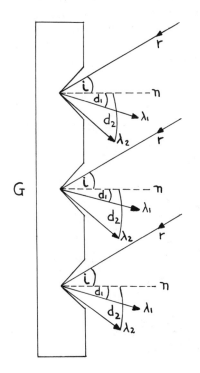

Figure 2-10. DIFFRACTION OF LIGHT BY A PLANE REFLECTION GRATING

G — grating; r — collimated incident ray; n — grating normals; i — angle of incidence; λ_1, λ_2 — diffracted wavelengths (λ_2 is longer than λ_1); d_1 — angle of diffraction for λ_1; d_2 — angle of diffraction for λ_2

In equation 2-6, which is applicable to all gratings, $\pm m$ is the *spectral order* (to be discussed later in connection with the concave grating), a is the distance between adjacent grooves, i is the incident angle of the light on the grating, and d is the angle at which a particular wavelength is diffracted.

$$\pm\, m\lambda \;=\; a\,(\sin i + \sin d) \qquad \text{(Equation 2-6)}$$

As an example, let us calculate the angle of diffraction for a light ray of 5000 A wavelength that strikes a 5900-grooves per centimeter grating at a 15° incident angle.

a (groove spacing) $= 1/5900 = 1.69 \times 10^{-4}$ centimeter
λ (wavelength) $= 5000 \times 10^{-8} = 5 \times 10^{-5}$ centimeter
Let m (spectral order) $= +1$
Substituting into equation 2-6 we have:

$$1 \times 5 \times 10^{-5} = 1.69 \times 10^{-4}\,(\sin 15° + \sin d)$$
$$\sin d = (5 \times 10^{-5} / 1.69 \times 10^{-4}) - \sin 15°$$
$$\sin d = 0.037$$
$$d = 2.12°$$

There are many types of concave-grating spectrographs all of which, with the exception of one, are based on the Rowland circle. One widely used type, the Paschen-Runge design in which the slit, grating, and camera are mounted in fixed positions on the Rowland circle (in contrast to the original Rowland design which provided for a movable grating and camera) is shown in Figure 2-11. The diameter of the circle is equal to the radius

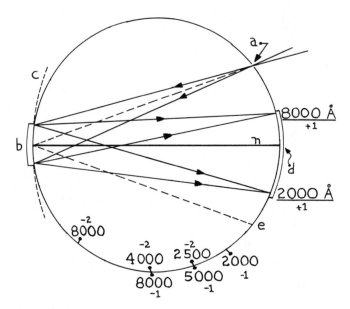

Figure 2-11. PASCHEN-RUNGE ADAPTATION OF THE ROWLAND CIRCLE
a — slit; b — grating; c — extension of the grating surface; d — camera; e — zeroth order (undiffracted slit image); n — normal to the center of the grating; $+1$ — indicates wavelengths of the first positive order; -1 and -2 — indicate wavelength of the first and second negative orders, respectively.

of curvature of grating *b*. Dotted line *c* is an extension of the mirror surface. Although not apparent from the diagram, the grating and circle have only one common point. Line *n*, which is the diameter of the circle and also the normal of the grating, is perpendicular to the tangent through the mirror-circle contact point.

Light that enters through slit *a* is diffracted in accordance with equation 2-6. Camera *d* is shown positioned to photograph spectral lines of wavelengths between 2000 and 8000 A. In contrast to the single spectrum formed by a prism, a grating produces many spectra each of which is called an *order*. The clear regions between the grooves reflect light, as does an ordinary mirror, and produce directly reflected beam *e* of the "zeroth" (undiffracted) order.

For reflection gratings, the sine of the angle of diffraction has a *negative* value if the incident and diffracted rays are on *opposite* sides of the grating normal. For example, the solution of equation 2-6 for the diffraction angles for all wavelengths less than 4370A yields negative values if the incident angle is 15°. Wavelengths greater than 4370 A are diffracted on the same side of the normal as the incident light and, accordingly, the sines of their angles of diffraction will be positive. The incident angle is always considered to be positive.

Spectral orders are formed on both sides of the direct beam and those on the side opposite the incident beam are designated as negative. To keep the spectrograph as compact as possible and for reasons of optical efficiency, only positive orders are photographed. In Figure 2-11. the first positive and first and second negative orders are shown. The two negative orders demonstrate how orders overlap and that the dispersion increases proportionately with the order number, i.e., second-order dispersion is twice the first order dispersion. A third-order spectrum has three times the dispersion of a first-order spectrum, etc. Chapter 4 describes ways to avoid possible confusion resulting from order overlap.

Some spectrographs are designed to take advantage of the higher second-order dispersion that is required when working with complex spectra. Spectral-order intensity decreases as the squares of the reciprocals of the odd integers, $(1/3)^2$, $(1/5)^2$, $(1/7)^2$, etc. In other words, a second-order spectrum is only 1/9 as bright as the first order and the intensity of the third order is 1/25 of that of the first. This sharp decrease in intensity makes it impractical to use spectral orders higher than the second or third except in specialized work.

A concave-grating spectrograph has a number of advantages over a prism instrument. Two of the most important are:

(1) The grating is self-focussing ; no auxiliary lenses are needed.

(2) The dispersion of a concave-grating spectrum varies only slightly

(by about 1%) with wavelength which simplifies the measurement of the wavelength of an unknown line. (This is true only if the angle of the incident light with respect to the grating normal is less than 20° and for diffracted wavelengths that fall within 15° of the normal.)

The reciprocal dispersion of a grating spectrograph varies inversely with the order number. For example, if the first-order reciprocal dispersion is 16 A/mm, the second-order dispersion is 8 A/mm.

As shown by equation 2-7, the resolving power R of a grating depends only on order number m and the number of grooves N that are exposed to the incident light.

$$R = m N$$ (Equation 2-7)

The resolving power required to separate the sodium D lines was shown by equation 2-4 to be 982. Applying equation 2-7, we have, for these two lines in the first order, $982 = 1 \times N$. This means that theoretically the separation can be accomplished by 982 grating lines. If a one-inch grating ruled with 15,000 lines were used, only 982/15,000 or 0.0655 inch of its ruled area would be required for the separation. As in prism instruments, the resolving power of grating spectrographs is also reduced by optical imperfections and is dependent on slit width.

Just as lenses and concave mirrors, in general, concave gratings are also subject to *astigmatism,* the inability to focus off-axis vertical and horizontal lines in the same plane. Consequently, spectral lines are in focus on the camera plane of the Rowland circle in width but not in length. This does not matter unless line height is of importance as, for example, in some methods of quantitative analysis, or when two separate spectra are to be photographed simultaneously.

Astigmatism can be substantially reduced by a number of devices.

(1) Sirk's focus

Figure 2-12 shows how this point can be located. A slit-height-limiting device or a comparison prism, which makes it possible to record

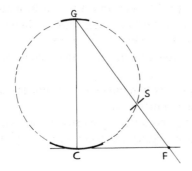

Figure 2-12. SIRK'S FOCUS FOR A CONCAVE GRATING
G — grating; S — slit; C — camera; F — Sirk's focal point (location of slit-height-limiting devices)

two spectra at the same time, is placed at intersection F of the grating-to-slit line GS and the tangent CF of the Rowland circle at the grating normal GC.

(2) Cylindrical lens

A lens of this type between the slit and grating, with its long axis at right angles to the slit, focusses an image of the slit length on the Rowland circle.

(3) Wadsworth's grating mounting

This concave grating system, the only one not based on the Rowland circle, is shown in Figure 2-13. Incoming light from slit S is collimated by mirror M, reflected to grating G, and the resulting spectrum is stigmatically imaged on a parabolic focal curve C that approximates a section of a circle whose radius of curvature is about one half the radius of the Rowland circle for the grating. Dispersion is accordingly reduced by 50% but the

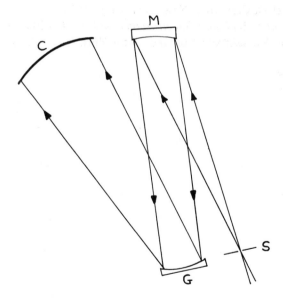

Figure 2-13. WADSWORTH'S STIGMATIC MOUNTING OF A CONCAVE GRATING

S — slit; M — collimating mirror; G — grating; C — parabolic focal curve (camera location).

resolving power remains the same as with the Rowland mounting. An ordinary collimating lens between the slit and grating has the same effect as mirror M but at the expense of instrument compactness.

REFERENCES

(1)   *Experimental Spectroscopy,* 3rd edition, R. A. Sawyer, Dover Publications, New York City (1963).

(2)   *Principles and Practice of Spectrochemical Analysis,* N. H. Nachtrieb, McGraw-Hill, New York City (1950).

(3)   *Practical Spectroscopy,* G. R. Harrison, R. C. Lord, and J. R. Loofbourow, Prentice-Hall, Englewood Cliffs, N. J. (1948).

(4)   *Certified Precision Diffraction Gratings,* brochure published by Bausch & Lomb, Inc. Rochester, N. Y. Describes manufacture of gratings.

(5)   *Diffraction Grating Handbook,* Staff of Bausch & Lomb Diffraction Grating Research Laboratory, E. G. Loewen, director, Bausch & Lomb, Analytical Systems Division, Rochester, N. Y. (1970).

(6)   *Analytical Emission Spectroscopy,* vol. 1, E. L. Grove, editor. Marcel Dekker, Inc., New York City (1971).

(7)   *Analytical Emission Spectroscopy,* vol. 1, J. Mika and T. Torak, Crane, Russak, and Co., Inc., New York City (1974).

CHAPTER 3

Representative spectroscopes and spectrographs

The instruments that have been chosen for discussion in this chapter are representative of those that are available in the low and medium price range from $200 to $15,000. Included are spectroscopes, combinations of visual and photographic instruments, and spectrographs. The effectiveness of these instruments for quantitative analysis ranges from rough to highly accurate.

Amici-prism-type hand spectroscope

Manufacturer—Bausch and Lomb

This direct-vision spectroscope, shown in Figure 3-1, is 95 millimeters long and 16 millimeters in diameter. It has an adjustable slit. Its

Figure 3-1. DIRECT-VISION HAND SPECTROSCOPE (COURTESY OF BAUSCH & LOMB, INC.)

angular dispersion is 6°15′ between the *C* and *F* lines. It can resolve the mercury doublet lines at 5769.6 and 5790.7 A. The instrument has an achromatic collimating lens but no telescope lens, the viewer's eye serving this function. Both emission and absorption spectra can be examined qualitatively and two spectra simultaneously by means of a comparison prism at the slit.

Bunsen-type spectroscope

Manufacturer—Bausch and Lomb

This spectroscope, shown in Figure 3-2, is a modern version of the original Bunsen model. Figure 3-3 illustrates its optical system. The index

Figure 3-2. BUNSEN SPECTRO-SCOPE (COURTESY OF BAUSCH & LOMB, INC.)

of refraction n_D of dense flint prism *d* is 1.62 and its viewing range 4000 to 8000 A. Its resolving power is adequate for the separation of the sodium doublet. Reference scale *i* is 15 millimeters long and divided into tenths of a millimeter. It is magnified fifteen times by eyepiece *g*. It requires an external light source *h* for scale illumination. Slit *c*, scale *i*, and eyepiece *g* are all focussable. The slit width is adjustable.

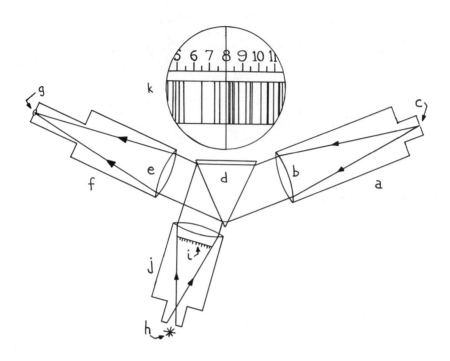

Figure 3-3 THE OPTICAL SYSTEM OF THE BUNSEN SPECTROSCOPE
a — collimating tube; *b* — collimating lens; *c* — slit; *d* — prism; *e* — telescope lens;
f — telescope tube; *g* — eyepiece; *h* — light source; *i* — reference scale; *j* — scale tube;
k — spectrum and scale as seen through the eyepiece.

Fisher Duo-Spectranal (patented) plane-reflection-grating spectroscope

Manufacturer—Fisher Scientific Co.

The Duo-Spectranal, shown in Figure 3-4, is a spectroscope designed for viewing the spectra of metals in solution. Its dispersing element is a 31,000-grooves-per-inch plane reflection grating. Its optical system is illustrated in Figure 3-5. Its reciprocal dispersion is 55 A/mm, with 3 A resolution. The stigmatic image formed by a plane grating allows two spectra to be viewed at the same time as shown in Figure 3-6. Wavelength scale *a* is calibrated directly in angstroms, the last two zeros being omitted, i.e., 53 represents 5300 A, etc. The instrument covers the visible spectral

Figure 3-4. FISHER DUO-SPECTRANAL GRATING SPECTROSCOPE
(COURTESY OF FISHER SCIENTIFIC CO.)

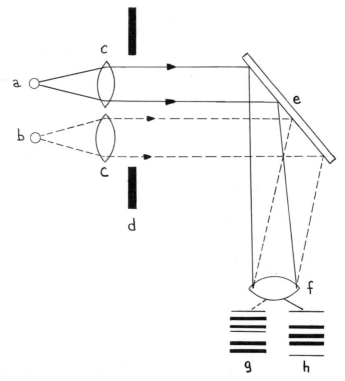

Figure 3-5. THE OPTICAL SYSTEM OF THE FISHER DUO-SPECTRANAL
SPECTROSCOPE
a − sample source; *b* − reference source; *c* − collimator lenses; *d* − slit; *e* − plane
reflection grating; *f* − eyepiece lens; *g* − reference spectrum; *h* − sample spectrum.

range from 3900 to 7000 A. Power requirements are 250 watts at 115 volts a–c, 50 to 60 Hz.

When voltage is applied between two platinum electrodes immersed in a small amount of solution containing the metals to be determined, there is a sparklike discharge consisting of a series of microscopic hydrogen and oxygen explosions. This electrically generated flame is intense enough to excite the neutral emission spectra of the dissolved metals. The slight heat generated is absorbed by a water jacket around the test tube containing the solution. According to the manufacturer, approximately sixty metals can be detected with the Duo-Spectranal at minimum concentrations that vary from 0.5 to 4000 parts per million, depending on the metal.

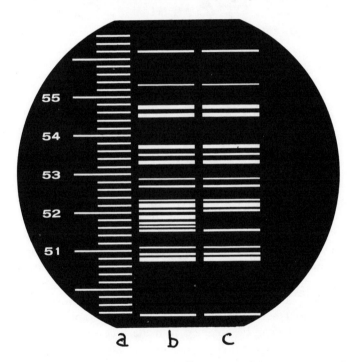

Figure 3-6. THE FIELD OF VIEW OF THE FISHER DUO-SPECTRANAL SPECTROSCOPE
a — wavelength scale; *b* — reference spectrum; *c* — sample spectrum.

Concave-grating-type Vreeland spectroscope/spectrograph

Manufacturer—Spectrex Co.

The optical system of this instrument is designed around a Paschen-Runge mounting as shown in Figure 3-7. Its 42.5-centimeter focal length,

15,000-grooves/inch grating gives a spectrum of 40.5 A/mm reciprocal dispersion. The wavelength range of the spectroscope, 4000 to 7000 A, can be extended in both directions to cover the 2500 to 8500 A region for photographic work. A unique feature of the instrument that facilitates viewing of the spectrum is the vertical plane of its Rowland circle rather than the conventional horizontal position. The power source, a simple, 115-volt a-c arc, is an integral part of the spectroscope. The power requirement is 1500 watts.

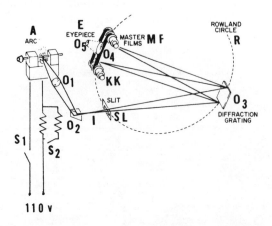

Figure 3-7. THE OPTICAL SYSTEM OF THE VREELAND SPECTROSCOPE

Figure 3-8 shows the standard eyepiece in position on the Rowland circle. It is moved up and down for viewing different parts of the spectrum and can be replaced by a camera. The multispectrum accessory at the left is fitted with a film mask that moves horizontally across the Rowland circle, allowing a series of spectra to be photographed side by side. Quantitative results can be obtained with the accessory at the right which is equivalent to a logarithmic sector at the slit (see Chapter 6). The spectrum is intercepted by an oscillating mirror and reflected to the film, producing spectral lines whose lengths vary with element concentration.

The Vreeland spectroscope is designed for use with reference spectrum films (MF in Figure 3-7) mounted on reels on the Rowland circle. The reference spectra (*b*) appear on either side of sample spectrum *a* as shown in Figure 3-9. An elaborate series of references is available, including films of spectra of individual elements, wavelengths scales, multiline element groups (doublets, triplets, quadruplets, etc.) key lines of the elements, and an iron reference spectrum.

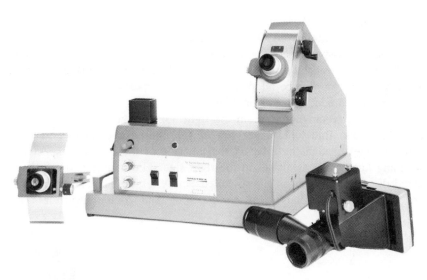

Figure 3-8. VREELAND SPECTROSCOPE WITH ACCESSORIES (COURTESY OF SPECTREX CORP.)

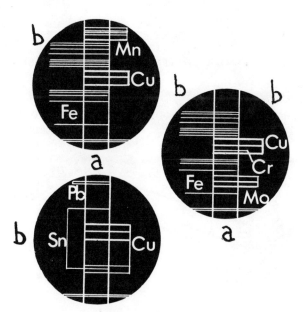

Figure 3-9. THE FIELD OF VIEW OF THE VREELAND SPECTROSCOPE
a — sample spectrum; *b* — line identification spectrum.

Prism-type Fuess spectroscope

Manufacturer—R. Fuess Co., West Berlin, Germany; American representative—Applied Research Laboratories

The Fuess spectroscope is representative of a number of instruments that have been designed primarily for the identification and sorting of alloys, although they can also be adapted to many other uses.

The instrument is shown in Figure 3-10. The optical components are located in the rectangular box on the right. On top, at the left of the eyepiece, is a disc that blocks the view of the unused eye. Light enters the spectroscope through the tube on the left side of the box. The spectrum-scanning knob, just visible, is on the right side. The sample and reference-metal discs can be seen on the so-called Petrey tables. The spectra of both are viewed simultaneously for comparison. The counterelectrodes (the

Figure 3-10. Fuess spectroscope (Courtesy of Applied Research Laboratories)

one below the right Petrey table is visible) are graphite discs that can be rotated to expose a fresh spot on the rim to the sample.

Figure 3-11, the optical system of the instrument, shows how light from sample and reference arcs 1 and 7 (from the latter via deflection prism 5) enters the spectroscope and is then directed by right-angle prisms 8 to dispersing prisms 12 and 14. The reflecting back of Littrow prism 14 returns the light through the prisms and, after two deflections by prism 10, the spectrum reaches eyepiece 9. The arrangement of the dispersing prisms results in three times more dispersion than would be obtained by a single passage of the light through a 60° prism. The spectrum is scanned by turning knob 13 which rotates prism 14.

The visible range of the Fuess spectroscope is 3900 to 7000 A. The instrument can be converted to a spectrograph by replacing the eyepiece with a camera which records the spectrum in three ranges; 3650 to 4230 A, 4230 to 4950 A, and 4950 to 6500 A. The midrange reciprocal dispersions

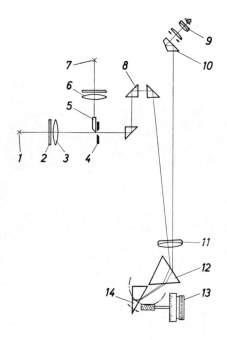

Figure 3-11. THE OPTICAL SYSTEM OF THE FUESS SPECTROSCOPE
1 — sample excitation arc; 2 — lens-protecting glass; 3 — condensing lens; 4 — slit; 5 — reference-beam deviation prism; 6 — condensing lens; 7 — reference excitation arc; 8 — deviation prisms; 9 — eyepiece; 10 — deviation prism; 11 — objective lens; 12 — dispersing prism; 13 — wavelength-setting drum; 14 — dispersing half prism.

are 4, 7, and 15 A/mm, respectively.

The power source is a high-frequency, spark-ignited, a-c arc generator that requires 230 volts a-c but can be adapted to 115-volt operation by using an auxiliary transformer.

The Fuess Spectravist is a similar instrument but it has greater dispersion and an optical system that allows visual comparison of line intensities for quantitative analysis.

Concave-grating-type A. R. L. Spectrographic Analyzer

Manufacturer—Applied Research Laboratories

The spectrographic analyzer shown in Figure 3-12 is a complete instrument package that includes a grating spectrograph, a d-c arc source, and a film viewer.

The optical system is shown in Figure 3-13. Its 0.885-meter-focal-length Wadsworth mounting is designed around a grating having 960 grooves per millimeter. The wavelength coverage is 4500 to 9300 A in the first order and 2250 to 4650 A in the second, with corresponding reciprocal dispersion values of 12 and 6 A/mm.

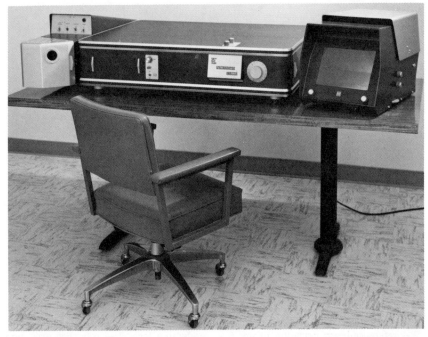

Figure 3-12. A.R.L. Spectrographic Analyzer (Courtesy of Applied Research Laboratories)

Spectra are photographed on a 35-mm film which is developed in a daylight processing tank. As the section of film in Figure 3-14 shows, up

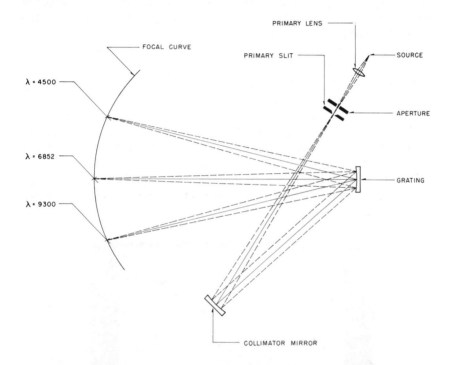

Figure 3-13. THE OPTICAL SYSTEM OF THE SPECTROGRAPH IN THE A.R.L. SPECTROGRAPHIC ANALYZER SYSTEM

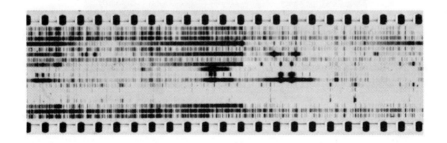

Figure 3-14. A SECTION OF A SAMPLE FILM PRODUCED BY THE A.R.L. SPECTROGRAPHIC ANALYZER (COURTESY OF APPLIED RESEARCH LABORATORIES)

to eighteen spectra can be recorded. An accessory turret at the primary slit carries a Hartmann diaphragm that allows three spectra to be photographed without moving the camera, a series of attenuation filters for varying the over-all intensity of an exposure, and a rotating logarithmic sector for quantitative work (see Chapter 6).

The power requirement of the excitation source is 2100 watts at 115 volts a-c, 50 or 60 Hz. Its current output is full-wave rectified at 5 and 10 amperes or half-wave rectified at 2.5 and 5 amperes. The arc is electrically ignited, i.e., it starts automatically.

As shown in figure 3-15, the film viewer displays simultaneously a magnified image (18X) of both the sample-film spectra and a master reference film. The latter includes an iron spectrum for checking the alignment of the sample and reference spectra, a scale for measuring the wavelengths of unknown lines, and the locations of the most-sensitive lines of the metallic elements by which corresponding lines in sample spectra can be identified.

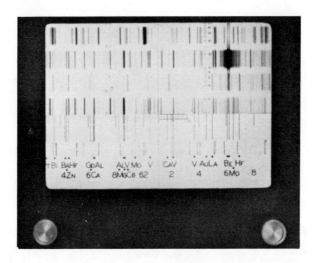

Figure 3-15. THE SCREEN OF THE A.R.L. SPECTROGRAPHIC ANALYZER FILM VIEWER (COURTESY OF APPLIED RESEARCH LABORATORIES)

Concave-grating-type (Paschen-Runge) Baird-Atomic Spectropac

Manufacturer—Baird-Atomic, Inc.

The Spectropac system includes a 1.5-meter grating spectrograph, a d-c arc source, and a microphotometer for measuring spectral-line transmission. Each component can be purchased separately.

The stigmatic Rowland mounting of the optical system is shown in Figure 3-16. Two gratings are available. One has first- and second-order reciprocal dispersion of 15 and 7.5 A/mm with wavelength coverage of 3700 to 7400 A in the first order and 1850 to 3700 A in the second. Corresponding figures for the alternate grating are 10 and 5 A/mm, 4500 to 7000 A and 2250 to 3500 A.

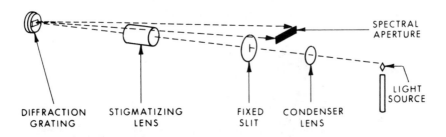

DIFFRACTION   STIGMATIZING   FIXED   CONDENSER   LIGHT SOURCE
GRATING   LENS   SLIT   LENS   SPECTRAL APERTURE

Figure 3-16. THE OPTICAL SYSTEM OF THE BAIRD-ATOMIC SPECTROPAK

The spectrograph with arc-stand enclosure and condenser lens mounted on an optical bench is shown in Figure 3-17. A Hartmann diaphragm in front of the slit permits photographing up to eleven spectra, one above the other, on the same film. The 35-mm film can be developed in a roll-film tank that does not require darkroom facilities. An

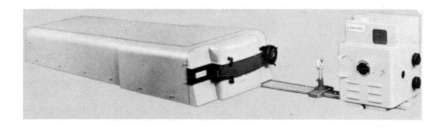

Figure 3-17. THE SPECTROGRAPH AND ARC-STAND ENCLOSURE OF THE BAIRD-ATOMIC SPECTROPAK (COURTESY OF BAIRD-ATOMIC, INC.)

"order sorter" in the optical system offsets first-order lines vertically by a fraction of a millimeter from those in the second order, making it possible to identify the order of a line immediately.

The d-c arc-power source operates from a 220-volt line. It is housed in a separate enclosure and is full-wave rectified with variable current, spark ignited, and includes a timer which controls the exposure time.

The microphotometer shown in Figure 3-18 projects an enlarged image of the apectrogram on its viewing screen. The degree to which the analytical lines transmit light (their relative blackness) is measured by a photocell circuit and indicated on the meter on the right. This information is converted to percentage values of elements as described in Chapter 6. The results that can be obtained from line-transmission measurements are more accurate than those by any other method.

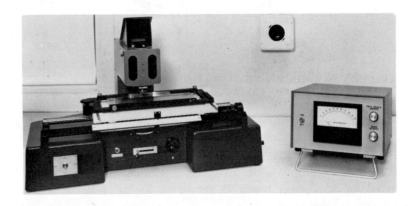

Figure 3-18. THE MICROPHOTOMETER FOR THE BAIRD-ATOMIC SPECTROPAK (COURTESY OF BAIRD-ATOMIC, INC.)

Manufacturers of emission spectrochemical equipment

Applied Research Laboratories
9545 Wentworth St.
Sunland, Ca. 91040

Gaertner Scientific Corp.
1204B W. Wrightwood Ave.
Chicago, Ill. 60614

Baird-Atomic, Inc.
125 Middlesex Turnpike
Bedford, Mass. 01730

Jarrel-Ash Div., Fisher Scientific
Co.
590 Lincoln St.
Waltham, Mass. 02154

Bausch & Lomb, Inc.
Analytical Systems Division
Rochester, N. Y. 14625

National Spectrographic Laboratories
19500 S. Miles Road
Cleveland, OH 44128

Fisher Scientific Co.
711 Forbes Ave.
Pittsburgh, Pa. 15219

Spectrex Corp.
3594 Haven Ave.
Redwood City, Ca. 94063

CHAPTER 4

The identification of spectral lines

An emission spectrum may consist of lines and *bands* superimposed on a continuous background of varying intensity. Line spectra are emitted by atoms and band spectra by molecules. A molecular band is composed of many individual lines that are closely spaced in the region of the band

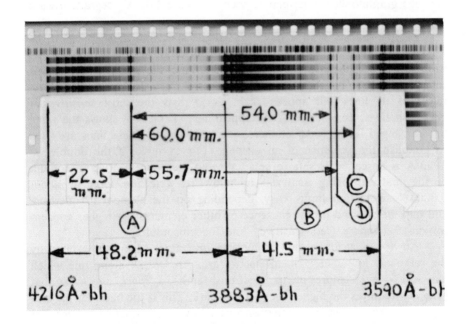

Figure 4-1 DEMONSTRATION LINE-IDENTIFICATION FILM
A — the 4057.8 A lead line; *B* — the 3683.5 A lead line; *C* — the 3639.6 A lead line; *D* — the 3671.5 A lead line; *bh* — cyanogen band head.

43

called the *band head*. Some band heads terminate sharply while others are more or less diffuse. In Figure 4-1, a molecular band head can be seen that terminates especially sharply at 4216 A. Band lines are more widely spaced as they recede from the band head. A band *degrades* toward the red or the violet, depending on whether the increased spacing is toward higher or lower wavelengths.

Among the factors that contribute to background intensity are radiation from incandescent particles in the arc, scattered light from internal optical surfaces of the spectrograph, and molecular bands. It is desirable that the background is just perceptible so that low-intensity lines can be detected. The upper spectrogram on the film in Figure 4-1 has low background intensity. In the four lower ones the effect of heavy molecular bands can be seen.

Molecular bands are used to identify a few elements, for example, boron in the boron oxide molecule and flourine in calcium fluoride, but for the most part they only obscure many valuable analytical lines. They can, however, be useful as wavelength reference points. The nitrogen in air reacts with vaporized carbon to form cyanogen molecules. The three major cyanogen bands that appear in the spectrum of an electric arc between graphite electrodes can be seen in Figure 4-1. All degrade toward the violet.

At first glance, even a relatively simple spectrum may appear to be a hopeless jumble of lines to the novice spectroscopist, but he soon learns to ignore all but those required to determine the composition of his sample. As the concentration of an element in a substance decreases, fewer of its lines will appear. Table 4-1* lists the most *sensitive* or *persistent* lines, i.e., those that disappear last. Table 4-2 shows the same lines arranged in the order of increasing wavelength. These lines are used to establish the presence of an element. For example, if the doublet at 5893 A is absent, it is safe to conclude that the concentration of sodium in the material being analyzed is below its *detection limit* of about 0.0001%. Detection limits vary, depending on the element in question, and may be affected by the presence of other elements. At higher concentrations, *secondary* (less-sensitive) lines become useful.

An *arc spectrum* is emitted by a *neutral* atom when it is excited by the relatively low energy of an electric arc. An *ionized* atom, one which has lost one or more of its electrons, emits a *spark spectrum* that generally requires the higher energy of a spark. This is the basis for the *arc-line* and *spark-line* classification of spectra. However, it is not a hard and fast rule, since many elements emit spark lines in an arc and vice versa.

---

* The tables referred to here are at the end of the chapter.

Lines are assigned relative-intensity ratings based on the 1 to 9000 scale of the *Massachusetts Institute of Technology* (*M.I.T.*) *Wavelength Tables*. The arc intensities of the 5890 and 5896 A lines, for example, are 9000 and 5000, that of a zinc line at 2771 A, 300, and that of an obscure iron line at 3599 A, 3.

Line identification with a spectroscope

A preliminary examination should be made to determine the general character of the spectrum, including its complexity and the presence of familiar lines. Highly complex spectra can be simplified by methods described in Chapter 7. Table 4-3 lists the most-sensitive visible lines that are emitted in an electric arc.

The wavelengths, as closely as can be determined from the wavelength scale of the spectroscope, of all the unknown lines should be recorded and the elements responsible for them tentatively identified by referring to Table 4-2 supplemented, if necessary, by a more complete table.

Reference spectra, those of materials known to contain substantial amounts of the elements that have been identified, should then be viewed. The presence of an element can be verified if at least two of its lines in the reference spectrum coincide with lines in the sample spectrum. Spectroscopes that are designed for viewing sample and reference spectra simultaneously are most convenient for identification work. Otherwise, the wavelength scale of the instrument must be used to check line coincidence.

Interference, the apparent coincidence of two or more lines because of insufficient resolving power of the spectroscope, must often be considered before a line can be positively identified. Let us assume that a spectroscope is able to resolve lines that are 1 A apart and that lines at 4723 and 5552 A have been detected which appear to be those of bismuth. A search for possible interfering lines may be conducted as follows.

The M.I.T. tables give the exact wavelength of the bismuth 4723 line as 4722.55 A. Interference could be due to any line within 1 angstrom on either side of this wavelength. In other words, the range of possible interference is from 4721.5 to 4723.6 A. There are forty lines listed in this range, two of which (very weak ones), in addition to the line in question, belong to bismuth. Several can be ruled out because they belong to gaseous elements and most of the others because their intensity rating is very low or they are lines of rare elements which are known not to be present in the sample. Only four lines, two of titanium, one of zinc, and one of chromium remain as possible interference candidates. None of these is a sensitive line. If sensitive visible lines of these elements have not been detected in the sample spectrum, they are also ruled out as interferences (since a secondary or weaker line of an element cannot be detected unless its sensitive lines are visible) and the 4723 A line can be established to be due to bismuth. If sensitive lines of even one of the three elements were present in the sample spectrum, the identity of the 4723 A line would be in doubt and have to be so reported. The 5552 A line should be analyzed for interference in the same way.

As the spectroscopist becomes familiar with the spectra of various types of substances, he learns to distinguish between *matrix* (major) elements and minor ones. As an example, let us assume that the intensity of the green copper lines at 5106, 5153, and 5218 A in a metallic sample is high and no other lines or only a few weak ones are visible. This spectrum immediately indicates a copper matrix sample or possibly pure copper. If, additionally, the blue zinc lines at 4680, 4722, and 4811 A and the red one at 6362 A were present, identification of the sample as a brass alloy would be logical.

A metal spectrum that shows the chromium and magnesium triplets at 5204-06-08 A and 5167-73-84 A, the five manganese lines between 4754 and 4824 A, and little else is almost certainly that of an aluminum alloy even though the persistent lines of the matrix element at 3944 and 3961 A may not be visible because they are too far into the ultraviolet.

An intense line does not always indicate a major element, however. The intensity of the sodium doublet, for example, even at the 1% level, far exceeds that of the persistent lines of most other elements that may be present at much higher concentrations. The 5890-96 A pair is an example of lines that *self-absorb* strongly. At higher concentrations of sodium, this effect becomes so pronounced that the lines *self-reverse* and one sees, instead of two yellow lines, two black ones (Fraunhofer dark lines) surrounded by a yellow halo.

The range of visual spectroscopy is limited by the response of the human eye to wavelengths between approximately 4000 and 7500 A. Consequently, most observers are unable to see the sensitive aluminum lines at 3944 and 3961 A and the sensitive silicon line at 3905 A. These elements are important because they are major constituents of many types of mineral and geological specimens. The fact that their lines cannot be detected visually is usually only a slight inconvenience, however, since silicon and aluminum are so widespread.

Information about a sample, such as its history, source, and classification (alloy, mineral type, etc.), should be considered, if available, before deciding on the presence or absence of a doubtful element. Lines in the spectra of rock samples, for example, can easily (and wishfully) be mistaken for those of gold or platinum both of which are rare. If for any reason, the presence of an element is unlikely, interference checks should be made.

Line identification in a spectrogram

Lines in spectra recorded on film are identified in the same general way as those in visual spectra. Spectrograms, however, can be studied at length and rechecked as many times as may be necessary in cases of doubt. Furthermore, film is sensitive to wavelengths down to about 2200 A which is significant because many sensitive and important secondary lines are found in the ultraviolet region.

The spectra on the film section in Figure 4-1 are those of a grating spectrograph with a reciprocal dispersion of 6.9 A/mm. The following calculations demonstrate how the wavelengths of lines are determined. All data are the result of measurements made with a millimeter scale through a magnifying lens.

VERIFICATION OF CYANOGEN-BAND-HEAD INTERVALS

$$4216 - 3883 = 333 \text{ A}$$
$$333/6.9 = 48.2 \text{ mm}$$

This corresponds exactly to the measured distance between the band heads at 4216 and 3883 A.

$$3883 - 3590 = 293 \text{ A}$$
$$293/6.9 = 42.5 \text{ mm}$$

In this case, the measured distance is 41.5 mm.

LINE A WAVELENGTH DETERMINATION AND IDENTIFICATION

The measured distance between the 4216 band head and line A is 22.5mm.

$$22.5 \times 6.9 = 155 \text{ A}$$
$$4216 - 155 = 4061 \text{ A}$$

Table 4-2 indicates a sensitive lead line at 4057.8 A.

LINE B WAVELENGTH DETERMINATION AND IDENTIFICATION

The measured distance between lines A and B is 54.0 mm.

$$54.0 \times 6.9 = 373 \text{ A}$$
$$4058 - 373 = 3685 \text{ A}$$

Table 4-2 indicates another sensitive lead line at 3683.5 A

LINE C WAVELENGTH DETERMINATION AND IDENTIFICATION

The measured distance between lines A and C is 60.0 mm.

$$60.0 \times 6.9 = 414 \text{A}$$
$$4058 - 414 = 3644 \text{ A}$$

Table 4-2 lists a lead line at 3639.6 A.

Lines A, B, and C are thus identified as belonging to lead. The differences between the calculated and actual wavelengths are within the limits of accuracy of this method of wavelength determination. Let us attempt to identify line D also.

LINE D WAVELENGTH DETERMINATION AND IDENTIFICATION

The measured distance between lines A and D is 55.7 mm.

$$55.7 \times 6.9 = 385 \text{ A}$$
$$4058 - 385 = 3673 \text{ A}$$

There is no line in Table 4-2 within a reasonable distance of 3673 A but the M.I.T. tables list a lead line at 3671.5 A with an intensity rating of 50. Since three sensitive lead lines have already been identified, line D could also be reported as due to lead.

The four identical spectra in Figure 4-1 are, in fact, those emitted by high-purity lead in a graphite arc. The top spectrum was produced with iron electrodes which accounts for the absence of the cyanogen bands. The range of interference due to the bands can be seen by comparison.

Higher-order spectra

The utilization of higher orders, mostly limited to the second order because of the rapid decrease in line intensity with increasing order number, makes it possible to work with spectra that are too complex for the first-order capability of a spectrograph. An instrument, such as the ARL spectrographic analyzer is designed for second-order ultraviolet and first-order visible-range work.

Order overlap can be a source of confusion, especially to the inexperienced spectrographer, but there are simple methods of overcoming this problem. Let us assume that we have to examine the 2400 to 3400 A region in the second order. All lines in this range will appear on the same segment of the Rowland circle as those in the first order between 4800 and 6800 A. By using film that is insensitive to wavelengths above approximately 4500 A, only the desired lines will appear on the spectrogram. Filters that are opaque to unwanted wavelengths can also be used to eliminate order overlap or a combination of a filter and appropriate film may be required. It should be kept in mind that dispersion in the second order is twice that in the first order.

TABLE 4—1

Sensitive spectral lines between 2000 and 9000 A excited in an arc source and listed in the order of decreasing sensitivity

Element	Line — A	Element	Line — A
Aluminum (A1)	3961.5	Barium (Ba)	5535.6
(425)*	3944.0	(472)	4554.0
	3092.7		4934.1
	3082.2		3071.6 x
	2575.1 x**		
	2652.5 x	Beryllium (Be)	2348.6
		(92)	3321.3
Antimony (Sb)	2528.5		3131.1
(524)	2877.9		3130.4
	2598.1		2986.5 x
	3232.5		
	3267.5 x	Bismuth (Bi)	3067.7
	2481.7 x	(344)	4722.6
			2898.0
Arsenic (As)	2288.1		2993.3 x
(257)	2349.8		2696.6 x
	2456.5		
	2780.2	Boron (B)	2497.7
	2860.5 x	(94)	2496.8

*The numbers in parentheses indicate the total number of neutral-atom and singly-charged-ion lines in the M.I.T. wavelength tables.

**Secondary lines for higher element concentrations are marked with an "x."

TABLE 4-1 (continued)

Element	Line – A	Element	Line–A
Cadmium (Cd)	2288.0	Cobalt (Co)	3453.5
(447)	6438.5	(1607)	3405.1
	3466.2		3044.0 x
	3261.1	Copper (Cu)	3247.5
	2980.6 x	(913)	3274.0
			5218.2
Calcium (Ca)	4226.7		5153.2
(662)	3933.7		5105.5
	3968.5		2961.2 x
	4454.8		3094.0 x
	4435.0		
	4425.4	Dysprosium (Dy)	4000.4
	3179.3 x	(2063)	4211.7
	2997.3 x		
		Erbium (Er)	4008.0
Carbon (C)	2478.6	(2039)	3906.3
***			3692.7
		Europium (Eu)	3930.5
		(2408)	4129.7
Cerium (Ce)	4186.6		4205.0
(5755)	4222.6		
	4296.7	Gadolinium (Gd)	3646.2
		(1607)	3362.2
Cesium (Cs)	8521.1		3350.5
(645)	8943.5		
	4555.4	Gallium (Ga)	4172.1
	4593.2	(135)	4033.0
			2943.6
Chromium (Cr)	4254.3		
(2277)	4274.8	Germanium (Ge)	3039.1
	4289.7	(73)	3269.5
	5208.4		4226.6
	5206.0		2651.2
	5204.5		
	2731.9 x	Gold (Au)	2428.0
	3015.2 x	(333)	2676.0

***Carbon is not ordinarily determined by emission spectroscopy. The 2478.6 A line, which appears in all graphite-arc spectra, is listed as a reference line for locating the spectrum region between 2400 and 2500 A.

TABLE 4-1 (continued)

Element	Line — A	Element	Line — A
Gold (Au)	3122.8 x		3639.6
(333)	2700.9 x		2663.2 x
			2476.4 x
Hafnium (Hf)	3072.9		
(1518)	2940.8	Lithium (Li)	6707.8
	2916.5	(39)	6103.6
	2898.3		3232.6
	2904.4		4603.0
Holmium (Ho)	3891.0	Lutecium (Lu)	4518.6
(800)	3748.2	(456)	2911.4
			2615.4
Indium (In)	4511.3		
(1150)	4101.8	Magnesium (Mg)	5183.6
	3256.1	(173)	5172.7
	3258.6		5167.3
	3039.4		2852.1
	2710.3 x		2795.5
			2802.7
Iridium (Ir)	2544.0		2779.8 x
(2577)	3220.8		2915.5 x
	3133.3		
	2662.0 x	Manganese (Mn)	4030.8
		(1395)	2801.1
Iron (Fe)	3719.9		4033.1
(4757)	3737.1		2576.1
	3745.6		4034.5
	3748.3		2933.1 x
	3020.6		
	2599.4 x	Mercury (Hg)	4358.4
	2994.4 x	(724)	2536.5
			5460.7
Lanthanum (La)	3949.1		3125.7 x
(1270)	4077.3		
	4123.2	Molybdenum (Mo)	3798.3
		(3902)	3903.0
Lead (Pb)	4057.8		3170.3
(466)	2833.1		3132.6
	3683.5		2816.2 x

TABLE 4-1 (continued)

Element	Line — A	Element	Line — A
Neodymium (Nd)	4303.6	Praseodymium (Pr)	4179.4
(2680)	4012.3	(2708)	4223.0
	4247.4		4225.3
Nickel (Ni)	3414.8	Rhenium (Re)	3460.5
(1176)	3493.0	(2256)	4889.2
	3524.5		
	3050.8	Rhodium (Rh)	3434.9
	3515.1	(1327)	3692.4
Niobium (Nb)			3280.6 x
(3303)	4058.9		3263.1 x
(formerly	4079.7		
called.	3094.2	Rubidium (Rb)	
Columbium)	3195.0	(365)	7800.2
			7947.6
Osmium (Os)	3058.7		4201.9
(1745)	2909.1		4215.6
	3040.9 x		
		Ruthenium (Ru)	3498.9
Palladium (Pd)	3404.6	(2824)	3436.7
(908)	3421.2		2678.8 x
	2922.5 x		2886.5 x
Phosphorus (P)	2535.7	Samarium (Sm)	4424.3
(408)	2553.3	(3863)	4296.8
	2554.9		3568.2
	2534.0	Scandium (Sc)	
		(524)	3911.8
Platinum (Pt)	3064.7		3907.5
(806)	2659.5		4023.7
	2650.9 x		4246.8
	2834.7 x		4020.4
Potassium (K)	7664.9	Silicon (Si)	2881.6
(306)	7699.0	(367)	2516.1
	4044.1		2528.5
	4047.2		2506.9
	3446.4 x		2435.2 x
	3447.4 x		2438.8 x

TABLE 4-1 (continued)

Element	Line − A	Element	Line − A
Silver (Ag)	3280.7		3262.3
(347)	3382.9		2863.3
	5209.1		2840.0
	5465.5		2421.7 x
			2813.6 x
Sodium (Na)	5890.0		
(175)	5895.9	Titanium (Ti)	3653.5
	3302.3	(2136)	4981.7
	3303.0		3349.0
			3341.9
Strontium (Sr)	4607.3		3372.8
(209)	4077.7		
	4215.5	Tungsten (W)	4302.1
	3464.6 x	(4327)	4294.6
	2931.8 x		4008.8
			2896.4
Tantalum (Ta)	3311.2		
(2164)	2714.7	Uranium (U)	4241.7
		(5238)	4543.6
Tellurium (Te)	2385.8		4090.1
(764)	2383.3		2882.7
Terbium (Tb)	4278.5	Vanadium (V)	3185.4
(2617)	4326.5	(3130)	4379.2
			3184.0
Thallium (Tl)	5350.5		3183.4
(300)	3229.8		2952.1 x
	2767.9 x		
	2826.2 x	Ytterbium (Yb)	3988.0
		(1254)	3694.2
Thorium (Th)	2837.3		
(2587)	4019.1	Yttrium (Y)	4374.9
		(686)	3710.3
Thulium (Tm)	3761.3		3242.3
(793)	3462.2		
	3761.9	Zinc (Zn)	6362.3
		(207)	3345.0
Tin (Sn)	4524.7		3302.6
(268)	3175.0		3282.3

TABLE 4-1 (continued)

Element	Line — A	Element	Line — A
Zinc (Zn)	4810.5	Zirconium (Zr)	4687.8
(207)	4722.2	(2036)	3392.0
	4680.1		3438.2
	2800.9 x		3601.2

TABLE 4-2

Lines in table 4-1 arranged in the order of increasing wavelength

Wavelength	Element	Wavelength	Element	Wavelength	Element
2200.		2500.		2700.	
88.0	Cd	35.7	P	80.2	As
88.1	As	36.5	Hg	95.5	Mg
		44.0	Ir		
2300.		53.3	P	2800.	
48.6	Be	54.9	P	00.9	Zn
49.8	As	76.1	Mn	01.1	Mn
83.3	Te	98.1	Sb	02.7	Mg
85.8	Te	99.4	Fe	13.6	Sn
				16.2	Mo
2400.		2600.		26.2	Tl
21.7	Sn	15.4	Lu	30.3	Pt
28.0	Au	50.9	Pt	33.1	Pb
35.2	Si	51.2	Ge	34.7	Pt
38.8	Si	59.5	Pt	37.3	Th
56.5	As	62.0	Ir	40.0	Sn
76.4	Pb	63.2	Pb	52.1	Mg
78.6	C	76.0	Au	60.5	As
81.7	Sb	78.8	Ru	63.3	Sn
96.8	B	96.6	Bi	74.2	Ga
97.7	B			77.9	Sb
		2700.		81.6	Si
2500.		00.9	Au	82.7	U
06.9	Si	10.3	In	86.5	Ru
16.1	Si	14.7	Ta	96.4	W
28.52	Si	31.9	Cr	98.0	Bi
28.54	Sb	67.9	Tl	98.3	Hf
34.0	P	79.8	Mg		

TABLE 4-2 (continued)

Wavelength	Element	Wavelength	Element	Wavelength	Element
2900.		3100.		3300.	
04.4	Hf	22.8	Au	11.2	Ta
09.1	Os	25.7	Hg	21.3	Be
11.4	Lu	30.4	Be	41.9	Ti
15.5	Mg	31.1	Be	45.0	Zn
16.5	Hf	32.6	Mo	49.0	Ti
22.5	Pd	33.3	Ir	50.5	Gd
31.8	Sr	70.3	Mo	62.2	Gd
33.1	Mn	75.0	Sn	72.8	Ti
40.8	Hf	79.3	Ca	82.9	Ag
43.6	Ga	83.4	V	92.0	Zr
52.1	V	84.0	V	96.9	Rh
61.2	Cu	85.4	V		
80.6	Cd	95.0	Cb	3400.	
86.5	Be			04.6	Pd
93.3	Bi	3200.		05.1	Co
94.4	Fe	20.8	Ir	14.8	Ni
97.3	Ca	29.8	Tl	21.2	Pd
98.0	Pt	32.5	Sb	34.9	Rh
		32.6	Li	36.7	Ru
		42.3	Y	38.2	Zr
		47.5	Cu	46.4	K
3000.		56.1	In	47.4	K
15.2	Cr	58.6	In	53.5	Co
20.6	Fe	61.1	Cd	60.5	Re
39.1	Ge	62.3	Sn	62.2	Tm
39.4	In	63.1	Rh	64.6	Sr
40.9	Os	67.5	Sb	66.2	Cd
44.0	Co	69.5	Ge	93.0	Ni
50.8	Ni	74.0	Cu	98.9	Ru
58.7	Os	80.6	Rh		
64.7	Pt	80.7	Ag	3500.	
67.7	Bi	82.3	Zn	15.1	Ni
71.6	Ba			24.5	Ni
72.9	Hf	3300.		68.2	Sm
82.2	Al	02.3	Na		
92.7	Al	02.6	Zn	3600.	
94.0	Cu	03.0	Na	01.2	Zr
94.2	Cb				

TABLE 4-2 (continued)

Wavelength	Element	Wavelength	Element	Wavelength	Element
3600.		4000.		4200.	
39.6	Pb	08.8	W	41.7	U
46.2	Gd	12.3	Nd	46.8	Sc
53.5	Ti	19.1	Th	47.4	Nd
83.5	Pb	20.4	Sc	54.3	Cr
92.4	Rh	23.7	Sc	74.8	Cr
92.7	Er	30.8	Mn	78.5	Tb
94.2	Yb	33.0	Ga	89.7	Cr
		33.1	Mn	94.6	W
3700.		34.5	Mn	96.7	Ce
10.3	Y	44.1	K	96.8	Sm
19.9	Fe	47.2	K		
37.1	Fe	57.8	Pb	4300.	
45.6	Fe	58.9	Cb	02.1	W
48.2	Ho	77.3	La	03.6	Nd
48.3	Fe	77.7	Sr	26.5	Tb
61.3	Tm	79.7	Cb	58.4	Hg
61.9	Tm	90.1	U	74.9	Y
98.3	Mo			79.2	V
3800.		4100.			
91.0	Ho	01.8	In	4400.	
		23.2	La	24.3	Sm
3900.		29.7	Eu	25.4	Ca
03.0	Mo	72.1	Ga	35.0	Ca
06.3	Er	79.4	Pr	54.8	Ca
07.5	Sc	86.6	Ce		
11.8	Sc			4500.	
30.5	Eu	4200.		11.3	In
33.7	Ca	01.9	Rb	18.6	Lu
44.0	Al	05.0	Eu	24.7	Sn
49.1	La	11.7	Dy	43.6	U
61.5	Al	15.5	Sr	54.0	Ba
68.5	Ca	15.6	Rb	55.4	Cs
88.0	Yb	22.6	Ce	93.2	Cs
		23.0	Pr		
4000.		25.3	Pr	4600.	
04.4	Dy	26.6	Ge	03.0	Li
08.0	Er	26.7	Ca	07.3	Sr

TABLE 4-2 (continued)

Wavelength	Element	Wavelength	Element	Wavelength	Element
4600.		5200.		6400.	
80.1	Zn	06.0	Cr	38.5	Cd
87.8	Zr	08.4	Cr		
		09.1	Ag	6700.	
4700.		18.2	Cu	07.8	Li
22.2	Zn				
22.6	Bi	5300.		7600.	
		50.5	Tl	64.9	K
4800.				99.0	K
10.5	Zn	5400.			
89.2	Re	60.7	Hg	7800.	
		65.5	Ag	00.2	Rb
4900.					
34.1	Ba	5500.		7900.	
81.7	Ti	35.6	Ba	47.6	Rb
5100.		5800.		8500.	
05.5	Cu	90.0	Na	21.1	Cs
53.2	Cu	95.9	Na		
67.3	Mg			8900.	
72.7	Mg	6100.		43.5	Cs
83.6	Mg	03.6	Li		
5200.		6300.			
04.5	Cr	62.3	Zn		

TABLE 4-3

Visible lines emitted in an electric arc

Aluminum — 3944*, 3962*
Antimony — 4034*
Barium — 4554, 4934, 5536, 5778, 6142, 6595
Beryllium — 4573
Bismuth — 4723, 5552
Boron — 5193†, 5440†, 5481†, 5790†   (oxide bands)
Cadmium — 4678, 4800, 5086, 6438

TABLE 4-3 (continued)

Calcium — 4227, 4455
Cerium — 4187*, 4628, 5512, 5523
Cesium — 4555, 4593, 6723, 6973
Chromium — 4254, 4275, 4290, 5204, 5206, 5208
Cobalt — 4793, 4814, 4840, 4868, 5301, 5343, 5992, 6450
Copper — 5106, 5153, 5218, 5782
Dysprosium — 4957
Fluorine — 5291 , 6064   (CaF bands)
Gadolinium — 4326, 4733, 5015, 5104, 5156
Gallium — 4033*, 4172*
Germanium — 4227, 4683
Gold — 4793, 5837, 6278
Hafnium — 4093*
Indium — 4101*, 4511
Iridium — 4426, 4616, 5450
Iron — 5167, 5233, 5270, 5328, 5371
Lanthanum — 4900, 4922
Lead — 4058*
Lithium — 6104, 6708
Magnesium — 5167, 5173, 5184
Manganese — 4754, 4762, 4766, 4783, 4824
Mercury — 4047*, 4358, 5461, 5770, 5790
Molybdenum — 5507, 5533, 5570
Neodymium — 5293, 5320
Nickel — 5477, 6177, 6191, 6256, 7122*
Osmium — 4420
Palladium — 4213, 5164, 5296
Platinum — 5060
Potassium — 6911, 6939, 7665*, 7699*
Praseodymium — 5111
Rhenium — 4889, 5276
Rhodium — 4375, 4529, 5599
Rubidium — 4202, 4216, 5725, 6071, 6206, 6298
Ruthenium — 4555, 5171
Samarium — 4760, 4816, 4884
Scandium — 5082, 5084, 5086, 5087, 5099
Silicon — 3906*
Silver — 5209, 5465
Sodium — 5890, 5896
Strontium — 4078*, 4216, 4607, 4876, 6878, 7070

TABLE 4-3 (continued)

Tantalum — 4813, 5403, 6021
Thallium — 5351
Thorium — 4920, 6409
Tin — 4525
Titanium — 4982, 4999, 5007, 5014
Tungsten — 5053, 5069, 5225
Uranium — 5915
Vanadium — 4827, 4832, 4852, 4865, 4876, 4882
Yttrium — 5087, 5972[†] , 6132[†]   (oxide bands)
Zinc — 4680, 4722, 4811, 6362
Zirconium — 4688, 4710, 4740, 4772, 4816

---

*Low eye sensitivity.
† Molecular band; wavelength of band head.

TABLE 4-4

Visible lines and molecular bands excited by the gas flame of a
laboratory burner

Element	Line wavelengths(A)	Band-head wavelengths(A)
Barium		5137, 5347, 5535
Boron		5193, 5440, 5481
Calcium		5544, 6182, 6203
Cesium	4556, 4593, 6213, 6723, 6973	
Copper		5050, 5240, 5370
Indium	4102, 4511	
Lithium	6104, 6708	
Manganese		many bands between 5100 and 5600
Potassium	4044, 4047, 6911, 6939	
Rubidium	4202, 4216, 6207, 6299	
Sodium	5890, 5896	
Strontium		6060, 6628, 6747
Thallium	5350	

TABLE 4-5

The most-sensitive visible lines of gaseous elements in a discharge tube

Element	Line wavelengths (A)
Argon	4300, 4339, 6965, 7067
Bromine	4705, 4785, 4817
Chlorine	4795, 4810, 4819
Fluorine	6856, 6902, 7038
Helium	4121, 4471, 5876, 6678
Hydrogen	4861, 6563
Iodine	5161, 5465
Krypton	4320, 4363, 4376, 5570, 5871
Mercury	4358, 5461, 5770, 5791, 6908
Neon	5401, 5852, 6402, 6507
Nitrogen	4110, 5667, 5676, 5680
Oxygen	4415, 7157
Xenon	4501, 4624, 4671

REFERENCES

(1) *Massachusetts Institute of Technology Wavelength Tables* (M.I.T. tables), G. R. Harrison, John Wiley, New York City. Over 100,000 spectrum lines of the elements between 2000 and 10,000A with arc and spark intensity ratings.

(2) *Chemical Spectroscopy,* 2nd edition, W. R. Brode, John Wiley, New York City (1943). Extensive practical wavelength tables.

(3) *Tables of Spectral Line Intensities,* N.B.S. Monograph 32, United States Department of Commerce, National Bureau of Standards, Washington, D. C. (1962). Part I — Arranged by elements; Part II — Arranged by wavelengths.

(4) *Handbook of Chemistry and Physics,* any recent edition, Chemical Rubber Co., Cleveland, Ohio. Sensitive lines of the elements; Standard wavelength tables; Flame spectra of the elements; Lines and bands emitted in flames of various gas mixtures.

(5) *Lange's Handbook of Chemistry,* any edition; Handbook Publishers, Inc., Sandusky, Ohio. Sensitive lines of the elements for qualitative analysis; interfering lines listed.

(6) *Spectrochemical Analysis,* 2nd edition, L. H. Aherns and S. R. Taylor, Addison Wesley Press, Reading, Mass. (1961). Most

sensitive lines emitted by the metallic elements in the direct-current arc; interfering lines listed.

(7)   *Practical Spectroscopy*, G. R. Harrison, R. C. Lord, and J. R. Loofbourow. Prentice Hall, Englewood Cliffs, N. J. (1948). Most sensitive lines of the elements arranged by elements and wavelengths.

CHAPTER 5

Accessory systems for spectroscopy

Spectrum excitation sources

A. Electrical

Qualitative and semiquantitative analysis can be done with the low-voltage a-c arc produced by the circuit shown in Figure 5-1 (a). A small arc welder can be adapted for this purpose. The construction of a source of this type is described in Appendix B. Special graphite electrodes containing a small amount of sodium chloride are required for maintaining the arc.

The direct-current (d-c) arc is a widely used source that combines high detection sensitivity with suitability for quantitative analysis. The simplest circuit of this type, shown in Figure 5-1 (b), consists of isolation transformer Ti which supplies about 230 volts to rectifier Rx. Inductance L stabilizes the arc and rheostat Rh controls the current which ranges from 5 to 15 amperes. Two arcs in series, one for the sample and the other for the reference substance, can be operated with this source when using a spectroscope that allows two spectra to be viewed simultaneously.

A low-voltage arc can be ignited by momentarily bringing into contact the electrode tips with a rack-and-pinion mechanism or similar device, or by touching both with the tip of a third graphite rod having an insulated handle.

The basic circuit of a high-voltage a-c arc that can be depended on to give good quantitative results is shown in Figure 5-1 (c). The values of $R, C,$ and $L,$ which typically vary from 0 to 200 ohms, 2 to 100 microfarads, and 50 to 400 microhenries, respectively, are chosen to provide the best circuit parameters for the analysis to be performed. A step-up transformer that supplies 10,000 volts or more and the appropriate combinations of $R, C,$ and L convert circuit 5-1 (c) to a spark generator that

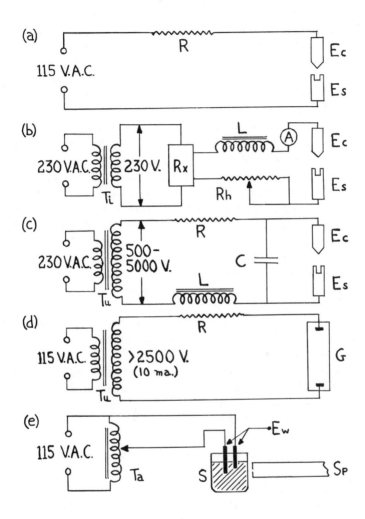

Figure 5-1. SPECTRUM EXCITATION SOURCES

(a) Low-voltage a-c arc: R — current-limiting resistance; Ec — counterelectrode; Es — sample electrode.

(b) Direct-current arc: Ti — isolation transformer; Rx — rectifier; L — stabilizing inductance; Rh — current-control rheostat; A — ammeter; Ec — counterelectrode; Es — sample electrode.

(c) High-voltage a-c arc: Tu — step-up transformer; R — resistance; C — capacitance; L — inductance; Ec — counterelectrode; Es — sample electrode.

(d) Gas-spectrum excitation source: Tu — step-up transformer; R — resistance; G — gas-discharge tube.

(e) Oxyhydrogen solution source: Ta — autotransformer; Ew — Platinum-wire electrodes; S — sample solution; Sp — spectroscope.

will give accurate quantitative results but whose detection sensitivity is not so good as that of an arc-type source.

The unidirectional interrupted arc is a hybrid source that combines desirable features of the d-c and high-voltage a-c sources. A rotating switch interrupts the current from a rectifier, for example, sixty times per second, and resistance-capacitance-inductance combinations give the source its desired oscillatory characteristics. This type of source is operated at outputs of 200 to 1000 volts.

High-voltage sources are ignited automatically by auxiliary electronic circuits. The electrodes are located in an enclosure whose door, when opened, actuates a switch that cuts off the power from the source.

Electrical excitation sources, especially high-voltage circuits, may be lethal and should be used with all the necessary precautions. Commercially built sources usually provide adequate protection. User-constructed or modified sources should be designed in the same way to include self-igniting arcs, shockproof electrode enclosures, proper insulation, fuses, etc. An arc should be viewed only through glasses, such as welders wear, or a window that adequately filters out ultraviolet radiation. An excellent way to watch the burning of a sample is by viewing an enlarged image of the electrode tips projected on a screen by a lens located behind the arc.

The spectra of gases at low pressures in glass tubes, called Geissler, spectrum, or gas-discharge tubes, can be excited by the circuit in Figure 5-1(d). Gas spectra are listed in Table 4-5.

The oxyhydrogen combustion system, the spectrum source for the Fisher Spectranal spectroscope, is shown in Figure 5-1(e). The construction and use of a source of this type, which is designed exclusively for solution analysis, is described in Appendix B.

B. Flame

The flame of a laboratory gas burner excites the visible lines and molecular bands of the elements listed in Table 4-4. A liquid sample can be introduced into the flame with a platinum-wire loop sealed into a glass rod, with an atomizer, or by means of a wad of cotton that has been saturated with the sample solution.

Up to seventy metallic elements can be detected with a much-hotter flame produced by oxygen or compressed air and acetylene. Burners specially designed for the gas mixture to be used are available from laboratory-equipment suppliers. The sample, in solution form, is sprayed into the flame with an atomizer either manually or with compressed air. Combination atomizer-burners that premix the gas and sample solution before they reach the flame are also available.

Electrode- and sample-support devices

Electrode and sample-support systems are shown in Figure 5-2. The arrangement in Figure 5-2(a), which is suitable for finely divided solids, consists of insulated post A that supports counterelectrode Ec and sample electrode Es.

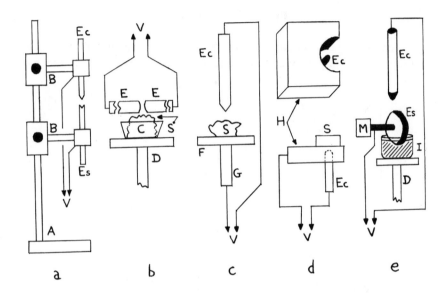

Figure 5-2. ELECTRODE- AND SAMPLE-SUPPORT SYSTEMS

System (a) A — insulated post; B — electrode holders; Ec — counterelectrode; Es — sample electrode; V — wires to voltage source.
System (b) C — combustion boat D — support platform; E — electrodes; S — sample; V — wires to voltage source.
System (c) Ec — counterelectrode; F — graphite platform; G — support post; S — sample; V — wires to voltage source.
System (d) Ec — counterelectrode; H — Petrey table; S — sample; V — wires to voltage source.
System (e) Ec — counterelectrode; Es — sample electrode (graphite disc); I — sample solution; D — platform; M — motor; V — wires to voltage source.

The Vreeland spectroscope uses the system in Figure 5-2(b). Sample S, in refractory combustion boat C (a refractory platform can also be used), is vaporized by the heat from the arc between horizontal electrodes E. Since no current passes through the sample, nonconducting materials can be analyzed by this method.

Substances that do conduct electricity can be arced on graphite platform F as shown in Figure 5-2(c). A *Petrey table*, Figure 5-2(d), is designed for supporting metal samples with a flat surface. The counterelectrode *Ec* is located below the sample which functions as a self-electrode. Metal discs in analysis position on Petrey tables are shown in Figure 3-10.

Liquid samples can be arced as shown in Figure 5-2(e). Graphite disc *Es* that is slowly rotated by motor *M* continually picks up solution which is transported to the arc between counterelectrode *Ec* and the highest point of the disc.

Types of electrodes

A carbon arc is maintained by carbon vapor which boils off from the tips of the graphite electrodes and conducts current across the gap

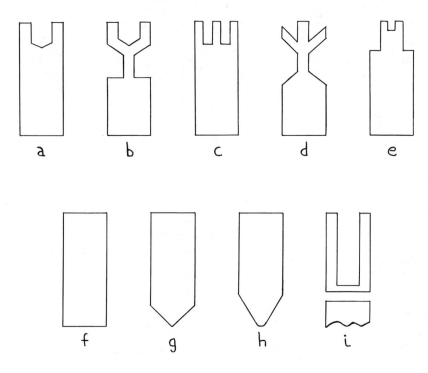

Figure 5-3. TYPES OF ELECTRODES

a — qualitative (sample); *b* — semiquantitative (sample); *c* — center-post (sample); *d* — platform (sample); *e* — microsample; *f* — flat-end (counter); *g* — quantitative, high-voltage (counter); *h* — hemispherical (counter); *i* — porous-cup (sample).

between them. Figure 5-3 shows the basic types of electrodes in cross section. Diameters vary from 1/2 to 1/8 inch, the 1/4-inch being the most commonly used.

Type *a* is suitable for the qualitative analysis of finely divided materials, such as powdered mineral samples.

Type *b* is a semiquantitative electrode. The undercut support post makes it easy to see when the sample crater has completely burned away so that the arc can be terminated without burning excess carbon which would cause an undesirable increase in the background density of the spectrogram. In addition, refractory materials are vaporized more efficiently in an undercut electrode because of the higher temperatures generated in the sample crater.

Type *c* with its crater center post is useful when a nonconducting sample makes it difficult to strike an arc.

Type *d* has a platform-shaped sample crater that gives good results in quantitative work.

Type *e* is used when only a very small amount of sample is available for analysis.

Electrodes *f*, *g*, and *h* are counterelectrodes. Type *f* is a graphite rod with a flat end. The arc has a tendency to wander around the edge of a tip of this shape. Type *g* is used with high-voltage arc and spark sources for quantitative work. Type *h* is widely used for both arc and spark sources.

A porous-cup electrode for solution work is shown in Figure 5-3*i* with a type *f* counterelectrode. The sample drips through the bottom of the cup into the arc.

Spectrographic-grade rods, sold in 12-inch lengths, can be cut and shaped as desired. All tools used for graphite work, such as hacksaw blades, drill bits, files, etc., should be reserved for that purpose only so that the electrodes will not become contaminated with foreign substances.

Type *g* counterelectrodes can be shaped with a pencil sharpener. Motor-driven counter-electrode shapers, with interchangeable blades, are available for shaping types *g* and *h*. Unless only a few are required, it is usually not worth while to attempt to make undercut electrodes. All types of preshaped electrodes can be purchased from suppliers of emission-spectroscopic equipment.

Optical-bench accessories

Electrodes, lenses, and any other accessories required between the light source and slit must be rigidly mounted on an *optical bench* so that they will remain fixed with respect to one an other and the spectrograph and centered on its *optical axis*, i.e., the line through the midpoints of the slit and the dispersing element.

The *variable-aperture sector* shown in Figure 5-4 is a device for reducing the total amount of light that enters the spectrograph to a level that produces a satisfactory spectrogram. Movable shutters control the size of the two openings in the sector which, together with its electric motor, are mounted on the optical bench in front of the slit. The sector should rotate at a minimum of 600 revolutions per minute.

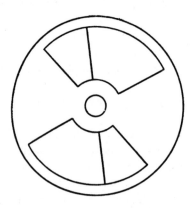

Figure 5-4. VARIABLE-APERTURE SECTOR

Other types of rotating sectors are used in quantitative work. They are positioned directly in front of the slit of a stigmatic spectrograph or at Sirk's focus (see Figure 2-12) in the case of an astigmatic instrument. Their use is described in Chapter 6.

Illumination

A spectroscope will usually give satisfactory results without an external lens for concentrating the light from the excitation source, whereas an auxiliary optical system is required to take full advantage of the capabilities of a spectrograph.

Maximum resolving power can be achieved only if the dispersing element (grating or prism) is illuminated over its entire width, and maximum spectral intensity requires its complete height to be exposed to light from the slit. In Figure 5-5(a) dispersing element D is only partially illuminated by light from source A (dashed lines). The illumination is complete when the source is moved to position B but this is usually not a practical solution because a hot source, such as an arc, may damage the slit C of the spectrograph. Figure 5-5(b) shows how the problem is solved with condensing lens L, which focusses an image of the source at point Bi.

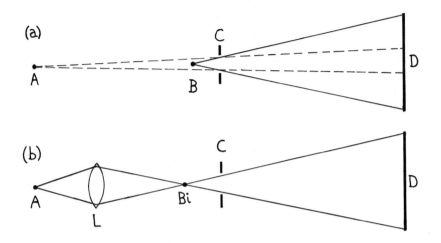

Figure 5-5. ILLUMINATION OF THE DISPERSING ELEMENT OF A SPECTROSCOPE

(a) Illumination without a lens A — excitation-source position that gives only partial illumination; *B* — excitation-source position that gives complete illumination; *C* — slit; *D* — dispersing element (prism or grating).

(b) Illumination with a lens A — excitation-source position; *Bi* — image of the excitation source; *C* — slit; *D* — dispersing element; *L* condensing lens.

Of the many auxiliary lens systems that have been proposed, one of the simplest and most effective is shown in Figure 5-6. Lens L is placed close to slit S and source A is positioned so that an image Ai of the arc is focussed on grating G. The images Ei of the incandescent electrode tips should be projected just above and below rather than on grating G where they would undesirably increase the background intensity of the spectrogram. This method of slit and grating illumination produces spectral lines of uniform intensity which is a requirement for quantitative work.

The source image may also be focussed on the slit rather than the grating in which case the intensity at each point on the slit and, consequently, that of the lines will vary with the intensity of the corresponding point in the arc since a carbon arc, especially a d-c arc, is by no means a uniform source of radiation. This type of illumination is useful for determining the part of the arc that is most suitable for a particular analysis.

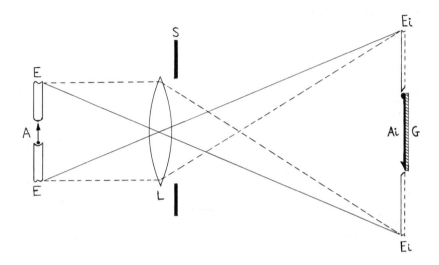

Figure 5-6. LENS ARRANGEMENT FOR UNIFORM SLIT ILLUMINATION
A — arc source; *E* — electrodes; *L* — lens; *S* — slit; *Ai* — source image, *Ei* — electrode-tip images; *G* — grating.

Photographic emulsions for spectrography

Spectrographic emulsions, available on 35-millimeter film in 100-feet rolls, are manufactured by Eastman Kodak Co. The most widely used is spectrum analysis (S.A.) No. 1 emulsion whose range of maximum sensitivity is 2500 to 4400 A. At lower wavelengths, the response of S. A. No. 1 drops off to a practical limit of about 2200 A. The insensitivity of this emulsion to visible wavelengths makes it ideal for second-order ultraviolet work since there is very little interference from first-order wavelengths greater than 4400 A. The fine grain, high contrast, and resolving power of S. A. No. 1 make it the best emulsion for quantitative work.

S. A. No. 3 emulsion is especially useful for the qualitative and semi-quantitative analysis of samples having constituents of widely varying concentrations, because it will satisfactorily record both very strong and very weak lines with a single exposure. Its range of maximum response is 2500 to 5000 A.

Type 103-0 is a very fast emulsion that is most useful for micro-samples having elements that emit weak line spectra or when the exposure time must be short. It is also most sensitive in 2500 to 5000 A region.

Type 103-F is similar to 103-0 except that its wavelength coverage extends to 6750 A. This makes it useful for the analysis of sodium and lithium.

Type 1-N is sensitive over the range of 2500 to 8750 A, the region that includes the most sensitive potassium, rubidium, and cesium lines.

Emulsion types S.A. No. 3, 103-0, 103-F, and 1-N are subject to second-order interference above 4400 A. This can be eliminated when the visible spectrum is to be photographed by placing a filter, such as Kodak wratten No. 2A, which cuts off wavelengths below 4000 A, in front of the spectrograph slit.

Film processing

For reliable results, spectrograms must be developed under standardized conditions, especially in quantitative work. The development time and the composition, temperature, and agitation of the processing solutions must be controlled.

The conditions given in Table 5-1 are generally satisfactory for all film types discussed.

TABLE 5-1

Processing conditions for spectrographic films

Process	Solution	Time (minutes)	Temperature (°F)
Developing (agitate continuously)	Kodak D–19 (or equivalent)	4	68
Rinsing (with agitation)	5% acetic acid	1	65 to 70
Fixing (with frequent agitation)	Kodak rapid fixer (or equivalent)	3 to 5	65 to 70
Washing	Running water	10*	65 to 70

* 20 minutes if the spectrogram is to be kept for future reference.

Working solutions should be renewed as required to maintain their strength so that the processing times in Table 5-1 do not have to be extended. Stock solutions will keep for much longer periods if they are stored in a refrigerator rather than at room temperature. This is also true of film which should be allowed to warm up to room temperature before being removed from its container, to avoid water condensation on the emulsion.

Except when a positive print is desired for illustrative purposes, the negative of a spectrogram is used for analytical work.

If a viewer-comparator or microdensitometer is not available, spectrograms can be examined through a magnifying lens or under a low-power microscope against a white background or on a frosted glass plate over a light source. A spectrum viewer with a track along which the lens or microscope holder can be moved to reach all parts of the spectrogram is a convenient aid.

Even better is an overhead or slide projector. The Bausch & Lomb Balmite 50 single-slide projector is ideal for this purpose. A film guide of the same thickness as a 35-millimeter slide is all that is required to adapt this projector for viewing 35-millimeter spectrograms.

The construction of a viewing system that includes a master spectrum with identification lines for the metallic elements is described in Appendix C.

REFERENCES

(1)   *Chemical Spectroscopy,* 2nd edition, W. R. Brode, John Wiley New York City (1943).

(2)   *Optical Methods of Chemical Analysis,* T. R. Gibb, McGraw-Hill, New York City (1942). Chapter 1.

(3)   *Experimental Spectroscopy,* 3rd edition, R. A. Sawyer, Dover Publications, New York City (1963).

(4)   *Practical Spectroscopy,* G. R. Harrison, R. C. Lord, and J. R. Loofbourow, Prentice-Hall, Englewood Cliffs, N. J. (1948).

(5)   *Principles and Practice of Spectrochemical Analysis,* N. H. Nachtrieb, McGraw-Hill, New York City (1950).

(6)   *Methods for Emission Spectrochemical Analysis,* any edition, American Society for Testing Materials, Phildelphia, Pa.

(7)   *Spectrochemical Procedures,* C. E. Harvey, Applied Research Laboratories, Glendale, Calif. (1950).

(8)   *Kodak Materials for Emission Spectroscopy,* Eastman Kodak Pamphlet P-10, 2nd edition, Eastman Kodak Co., Rochester, N. Y.

CHAPTER 6

Quantitative, semiquantitative, and qualitative analysis

Quantitative spectrochemical analysis takes advantage of the fact that the intensities of certain lines in the spectrum of each element, called *analytical lines,* are proportional to the concentration (%) of the element in the sample being analyzed.

To be suitable for quantitative determination, an ideal spectrum line should

(1) not be subject to interference from background or other lines.

(2) not self-absorb over the expected concentration range of the element.

(3) register on the photographic emulsion in degrees of blackness (intensity) that are proportional to the concentration of the element it represents.

These requirements are based on the assumption that the many factors affecting line intensity, such as optical, electrical, and mechanical conditions of the spectrograph, remain constant. However, this is rarely the case. Uncontrollable changes may occur at any time causing line-intensity variations that are not related to concentration differences.

This difficulty is overcome by working with the ratio of the intensity of an analytical line to that of a reference or *internal standard line* which may be a line of one of the other elements in the sample, often a major element, or a line of an element that is added to the sample for providing a suitable internal standard line. In any case, the concentration of the reference element is essentially a constant of the analytical system, so that, at a given concentration of the element being determined, even though the absolute intensities of the analytical and internal standard lines may vary, their ratio remains the same. The factors responsible for the variations affect both lines to the same degree; for example, the intensities of both may increase by 10% or decrease by 5% compared to their levels during an earlier analysis.

A *working curve,* Figure 6-1, is constructed by plotting intensity ratios *versus* element concentrations for several *standards,* samples of known composition, on logarithmic coordinates. A perfect working curve has a 45° slope and is linear over its entire length. The degree to which departures from the ideal can be tolerated depends on the analytical accuracy required.

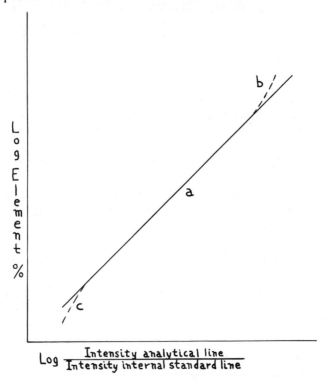

Figure 6-1. A WORKING CURVE

a — linear part of the curve; *b* — nonlinearity due to self-absorption of the analytical line; *c* — nonlinearity due to background or a line that interferes with the analytical line

Nonlinearity at the high end of a working curve, dashed line *b,* is usually due to self-absorption of the analytical line. At the low end, line *c,* it may be due to interference from background radiation or an unsuspected line whose wavelength is practically the same as that of the analytical line.

Line pairs that give satisfactory working curves are called *homologous pairs*. As far as possible, the members of a homologous pair should be

(1) in the same region of the spectrum, because the response of a photographic emulsion is not the same at all wavelengths.

(2) of approximately equal intensity at the midpoint of the working curve.

(3) of the same type, i.e., both should be either arc lines or spark lines.

The choice of suitable lines for an analysis is a problem for the spectrographer only when a published method, which always specifies line pairs, is not available.

At least three standards are required for the construction of a working curve to make possible the detection of any departure from linearity. They should furnish a high-, medium-, and low-concentration point for the curve and be of the same general composition as the samples to be analyzed.

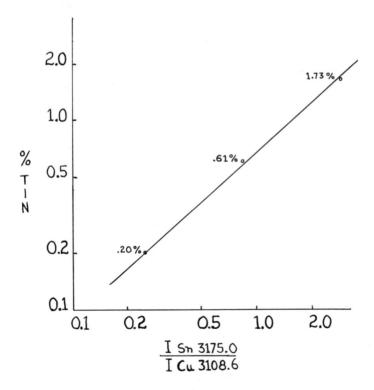

Figure 6-2. WORKING CURVE FOR TIN IN YELLOW BRASS

As an example of the construction of a working curve, let us assume that a metal foundry that analyzes its metals spectrographically is making 70/30 yellow-brass castings (approximately 70% copper and 30% zinc) whose tin content must fall between the limits of 0.50 and 1.50%.

Three 70/30 standards are prepared, with tin concentrations of approximately 0.25%, 0.75%, and 1.75%, and their spectra photographed. For each standard, the intensity of the analytical line, tin-3175.0 A, and internal standard line, copper-3108.6 A, is measured, the intensity ratios are calculated, and a working curve similar to the one in Figure 6-2 is plotted.

Any 70/30 brass sample can now be analyzed by obtaining from the curve the tin concentration corresponding to the intensity ratio of its tin-3175.0 and copper-3108.6 lines.

Working-curve shifts, a common occurrence, are compensated for by rephotographing standard spectra at regular intervals and replotting the curve.

Methods of measuring spectrum-line intensities

If a *logarithmic sector,* a circular disc whose perimeter has been cut to the shape of a logarithmic spiral, is placed with respect to spectrograph slit *S* as shown in Figure 6-3 and rotated at speeds greater than 600 revolutions per minute, the spectrum lines generated turn out to be wedge shaped rather than rectangular. Under these conditions, the length of a line is proportional to its intensity and, since the difference between the logarithms of two numbers is equal to the logarithm of the ratio of the numbers, the difference between the lengths of the analytical and internal standard lines of a homologous pair is proportional to the logarithm of their intensity ratio.

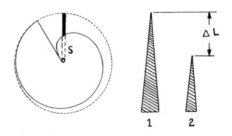

Figure 6-3. LOGARITHMIC SECTOR

s – spectrograph slit; *1* – analytical line; *2* – internal standard line; ΔL – difference between lengths of lines *1* and *2*

Working curves can be plotted on either semilogarithmic or linear coordinates as shown in Figure 6-4. Positive ordinate values indicate intensity ratios greater than one, negative values, ratios less than one, and zero on the ordinate represents unity intensity ratio since the logarithm of one is zero.

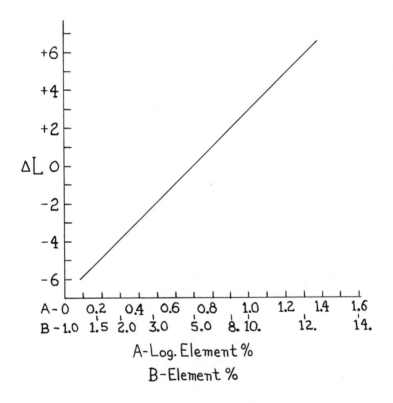

Figure 6-4. WORKING CURVE FOR THE LOGARITHMIC-SECTOR METHOD
ΔL – difference in length between analytical and internal standard lines.

As explained in Chapter 2, a logarithmic sector should be placed directly in front of the slit if the spectrograph is stigmatic but must be at the Sirk's focus position if the instrument is astigmatic. In either case, the slit must be uniformly illuminated (See Chapter 5).

A line length can be measured with an eyepiece or a low-power microscope equipped with an engraved measuring scale calibrated in tenths of a millimeter or thousandths of an inch. Alternatively, an enlarged image of the spectrum can be projected onto a screen for line measurement.

Lines do not terminate sharply but fade out gradually which accounts for most of the 10% error inherent in the logarithmic-sector method of analysis. Some spectrographers estimate the termination point by eye alone and others use an artifical reference line for comparison but whichever method is used, it should be applied consistently.

Quantitative analysis based on line blackness (more accurately, line *density*) rather than length may give results that are within 1% of element concentration. The amount of light transmitted by a spectrum line is measured electronically with a *microphotometer,* also called a *microdensitometer.* Its essential features are shown in Figure 6-5. Line *d,* whose transmission is to be measured, is centered in the light path of the microphotometer and *e,* a scanning device that has a slit *f,* which is narrower and shorter than the line, scans the line in the direction of arrow *g.*

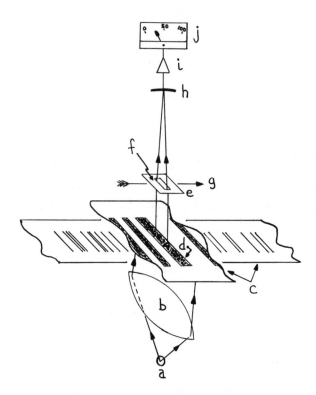

Figure 6-5. COMPONENTS OF A MICRODENSITOMETER

a − microphotometer light source; *b* − condensing lens; *c* − spectrogram film; *d* − spectrum line whose transmission is being measured; *e* − line scanner; *f* − scanner slit; *g* − scanning direction; *h* − photocell; *i* − current amplifier; *j* − meter.

The change in current through photocell *h* as the line is scanned is amplified by *i* and registers on meter *j*. The minimum meter reading indicates the amount of light transmitted by the line compared to the transmission of the clear film which is considered 100%. Transmission values are converted to line intensities (the *relative* intensity of the light responsible for a line) by means of an *emulsion-calibration curve*.

Construction of an emulsion-calibration curve

METHOD 1. *Two-step filter*

This procedure uses a quartz optical filter *b* of the type shown in Figure 6-6A, half of which is coated with a thin metallic film *1* that transmits only about half as much light as the uncoated section *2*. In an astigmatic

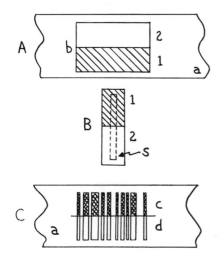

Figure 6-6. TWO-STEP EMULSION-CALIBRATION FILTER
A — Filter in front of film: a — film: *b —* filter; *1 —* metallized half of filter; *2 —* clear half of filter.
B — Filter in front of spectrograph slit: s — slit; *1 —* metallized half of filter; *2 —* clear half of filter.
C — Split-intensity spectrogram: a — film; *c —* unfiltered half-lines (darker); *d —* filtered half-lines (lighter).

spectrograph, the filter, which is about 1 1/2 inches long, is placed almost in contact with the film in the region of the spectrum that includes the lines involved in the analysis. Assuming the dispersion of the instrument to be 16 A/mm, about a 610 A span of the spectrum would be covered by the filter ($16 \times 25.4 \times 1.5 = 610$). A narrower two-step filter may be placed in front of slit *s* of a stigmatic spectrograph, as shown in Figure 6-6B. In both cases, the slit must be uniformly illuminated.

Figure 6-6C shows the split-intensity lines produced by a two-step filter. Darker half *c* is due to the clear section of the filter and the metallized area is responsible for lighter half *d* of each line. Since a slit filter intercepts all of the light that enters the spectrograph, the entire spectrogram consists of two-intensity-level lines when a two-step slit filter is used.

A direct-current-arc iron spectrum is photographed with 1/4-inch iron rods or heavy nails as electrodes. Current and exposure time are adjusted so that spectrum lines of varying intensities over the entire transmission range will be available in the desired wavelength region. After development under standardized conditions, as described in Chapter 5, the film is placed in a microphotometer and the transmission of both the filtered and unfiltered halves of about twenty lines is measured after the instrument has been adjusted to read 100 on clear film. The results are recorded as shown in Table 6-1.

TABLE 6-1

Line	Unfiltered half	Filtered half
1	69.0	89.0
2	16.0	38.5
3	26.5	54.5
4	9.0	23.5
5	3.0	7.5
6	83.5	95.0
7	40.0	69.0
8	58.0	83.5

The filtered transmission readings are plotted as abscissa values against the corresponding unfiltered ones on linear-coordinate paper as shown in Figure 6-7 and a smooth *preliminary* curve is drawn that passes through the origin and 100-100 point. The final calibration curve is constructed as follows.

Starting with the transmission value of 2 on the ordinate, the corresponding filtered value of 5 is read on the abscissa. Applying 5 to the ordinate again gives 12.5 on the abscissa, etc. This process can be repeated seven times to obtain a final filtered value of 95.5.

Let us assume that the metallized part of the two-step filter transmits only 59% as much light as the uncoated half. Then, since the reciprocal of 0.59 is 1.69, each filtered transmission value that has been obtained from the preliminary curve represents a relative light-intensity level that is 1.69 times greater than the preceding one. These results, summarized in Table 6-2, are equivalent to those that would be obtained with a seven-step filter whose transmission varies by a factor of 1.69 from step to step.

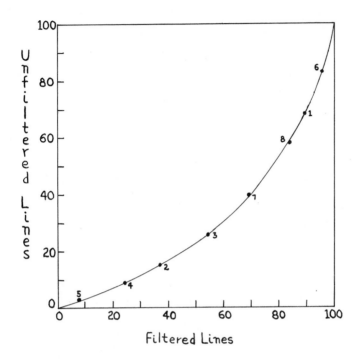

Figure 6-7. GRAPH OF DATA IN TABLE 6-1   (PRELIMINARY EMULSION-CALIBRATION CURVE) NUMBERS ON CURVE ARE LINE NUMBERS IN TABLE 6-1

TABLE 6-2

Relative intensities of filtered transmission values read
from the preliminary curve

Step (n)	Relative intensity 1.69^n	% Transmission
1	1.69	95.5
2	2.85	84.5
3	4.83	60.5
4	8.16	31.0
5	13.79	12.5
6	23.30	5.0
7	39.38	2.0

Plotting the data in Table 6-2 logarithmically gives the final emulsion-calibration curve of Figure 6-8, which is used to convert line-transmission readings to relative light-intensity values.

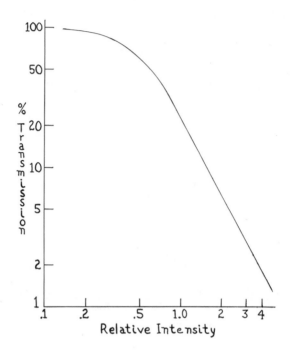

Figure 6-8. FINAL EMULSION-CALIBRATION CURVE
The relative intensity values in Table 6-2 have been reduced by a factor of 10.

Table 6-3 shows how intensity ratios for Figure 6-2 are calculated with the calibration curve, using assumed transmission readings for the tin and copper lines of the yellow-brass standards.

TABLE 6-3

The conversion of transmission readings for the tin and copper lines of the standards in Figure 6-2 to relative intensities and the calculation of intensity ratios

% Tin in standard	Line-transmission reading		Relative intensity of line from calibration curve		Intensity ratio Sn 3175/Cu 3108
	Sn-3175 A	Cu-3108 A	Sn-3175	Cu-3108	
0.20	88	21	0.25	1.02	0.245
0.62	21	15	1.02	1.23	0.830
1.73	4	24	2.57	0.93	2.76

METHOD *2. Rotating step sector*

A step sector is a disc whose perimeter has been cut, as shown in Figure 6-9, to form a number of (in this case, five) circular steps. The

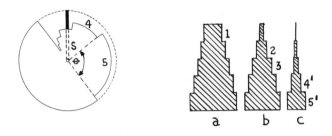

Figure 6-9. STEP SECTOR FOR EMULSION CALIBRATION

s — spectrograph slit; *5* — the longest sector step; θ — the angle subtended by step *5*; *4* — the second-longest sector step; *a* — the most intense of three lines photographed with the step sector; *1* — the line step produced by the shortest sector step; *b* — the line of intermediate intensity; *2* — the line step produced by the second-shortest sector step; *3* — the line step produced by the middle sector step; *c* — the least intense line; *4'* — the line step produced by sector step *4*; *5'* — the line step produced by sector step *5*.

angles subtended by the arcs of adjacent steps have a constant ratio to each other called a *step factor.*

If, for example, θ, the angle subtended by step 5 is assigned a relative value of 16, then, for a step factor of 2, the magnitudes of the angles of the remaining steps will be 8, 4, 2, and 1, respectively. In other words, as the sector rotates, step 5 takes sixteen times longer to pass spectrograph slit *s* than step 1, eight times longer than step 2, etc. The variations in the amount of light that enters the slit produce step-shaped spectral lines similar to *a, b,* and *c.* Fewer steps may appear in a weak line than in a stronger one and a longer sector step produces a denser (blacker) and wider line step than a shorter one.

Let us assume that the results of transmission measurements on each of the steps in the lines illustrated in Figure 6-9 are as shown in Table 6-4.

Plotting the data in Table 6-4 on logarithmic coordinates will yield three curves, as shown in Figure 6-10. Since the step-intensity ratio is the same for all three lines, the curves may be considered horizontally displaced sections of the same curve. This displacement is due to the over-all intensity differences between the lines.

TABLE 6-4
Transmission of line steps in Figure 6-9

Line step	Step transmission reading			Relative intensity of step
	Line a	Line b	Line c	
1	40	67	95	1
2	20	46	87	2
3	11	26	71	4
4'	6	14	50	8
5'	3	7	29	16

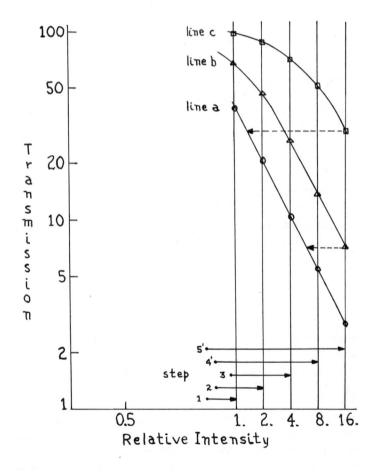

Figure 6-10. GRAPHS OF LINE-TRANSMISSION DATA IN TABLE 6-4

If the curves for lines *b* and *c* are moved horizontally to the left as indicated by the dashed lines, which can be done since we are concerned only with *relative* intensities that are not affected by this shift, they will coincide to form the single, composite emulsion-calibration curve shown in Figure 6-11. To make the calibration curve more accurate, additional points can be obtained by measuring more lines with the densitometer.

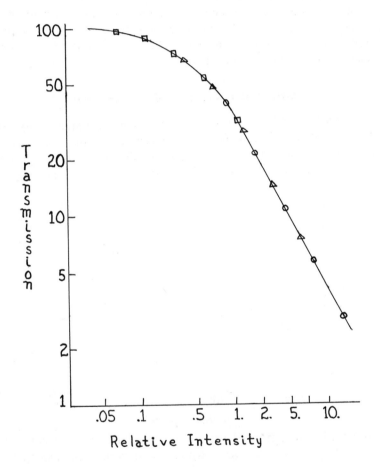

Figure 6-11. FINAL (COMPOSITE) EMULSION-CALIBRATION CURVE OBTAINED BY THE STEP-SECTOR METHOD

As with other devices involving line height, uniform slit illumination is important when a step sector is used and it must be placed at Sirk's focal point if the spectrograph is astigmatic.

Attenuation filters

It is often necessary to reduce the over-all intensity of a spectrum before quantitative results can be obtained. This is done with a metallized *neutral* slit filter that attenuates all wavelengths equally, for example, by 25% or 50%. The variable-aperture sector shown in Figure 5-4 has the same effect on spectrum intensity.

Line filters of about 1/8-inch width are also used to attenuate specific lines. They are mounted in the spectrograph camera close to the film and centered on the line whose intensity is to be reduced. Filters with attenuation factors of 5 to 50% are available.

Gamma of spectrographic emulsions

The slope of the linear portion of an emulsion-calibration curve, called gamma in photographic terminology, is a measure of the contrast of the emulsion—its response to changes in light intensity. Figure 6-12 shows how the gamma of S.A. No. 1 and S.A. No. 3 film varies with wavelength.

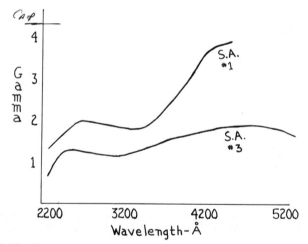

Figure 6-12. VARIATION IN THE VALUE OF GAMMA WITH WAVELENGTH FOR S.A. NO. 1 AND S.A. NO. 3 KODAK SPECTROGRAPHIC EMULSIONS

Both emulsions require frequent calibrations at low wavelengths, S.A. No. 1 over the 2200 to 2700 A range and S.A. No. 3 between 2200 and 2500 A. Fewer are necessary for S.A. No. 1 between 2700 and 3500 A and, in routine work, one is usually adequate for S.A. No. 3 film over the 2400 to 3500 A range. At wavelengths greater than 3500 A, frequent calibrations are again required for both emulsions, especially for S.A. No. .1

Because of the work involved in constructing calibration curves, if possible, the lines required for an analysis should be chosen so that they will be in a wavelength region covered by a single curve. Although S.A. No. 3 emulsion has a relatively constant gamma over the 2400 to 3500 A range, where analytical lines for many elements are located, S.A. No. 1 is preferable for quantitative work when greatest accuracy is required because of its higher contrast and smaller grain size, factors that allow more-accurate line-transmission readings.

Calculating boards

When many intensity ratios have to be calculated, it is time consuming to have to convert transmission to intensity for each line and then

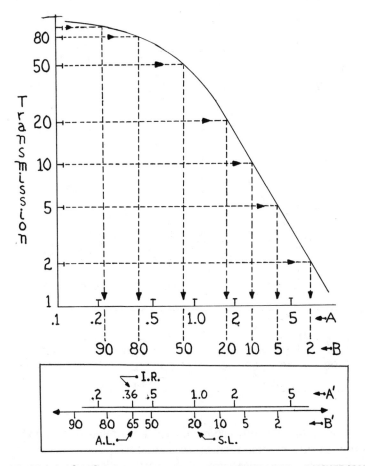

Figure 6-13. CALCULATING-BOARD LAYOUT FOR CONVERSION OF LINE-TRANSMISSION READINGS TO INTENSITY RATIOS

A — relative-intensity scale; B — projected transmission scale; A' — scale A on fixed calculator strip; B' — scale B on sliding calculator strip; $A.L.$ — transmission of analytical line; $S.L.$ — transmission of internal-standard line; $I.R.$ — intensity ratio, $A.L./S.L.$

calculate the ratios. Figure 6-13 shows the layout of a calculating board that reduces the operation to a single step.

The transmission scale is projected to the abscissa of the emulsion-calibration curve, as shown, to form scale B which is then transferred as

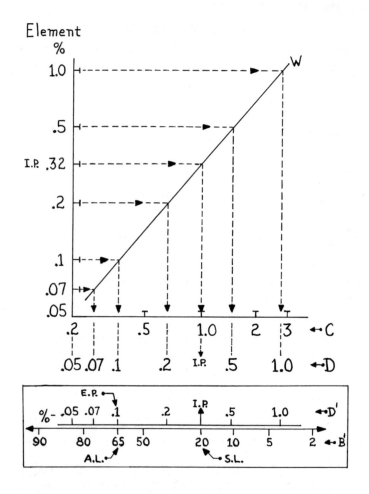

Figure 6-14. CALCULATING BOARD FOR DIRECT CONVERSION OF INTENSITY RATIOS TO PERCENTAGE OF ELEMENT

I.P. — index point of working curve; C — intensity-ratio scale of working curve (must coincide with scale A in Figure 6-13) D — projected element percentage scale; D' — scale D on fixed calculator strip; B' — scale B (from figure 6-13) on sliding calculator strip; W — working curve; *E.P.* — element concentration; *A.L.* — transmission of analytical line; *S.L.* — transmission of internal-standard line.

scale B' to a wood or metal strip that slides in horizontal tracks like a slide-rule cursor. Scale A' is the intensity scale A transferred to a similar *fixed* strip.

An intensity ratio is determined by aligning the transmission of the internal-standard line $S.L.$ on scale B' with 1.0 on scale A' and reading the ratio $I.R.$ on A' above the analysis-line transmission $A.L.$ on B'. The calculator, which works like a slide rule, is shown indicating an intensity ratio of 0.36 for standard- and analysis-line transmissions of 20 and 65, respectively.

The final result, the percentage of an element, is obtained by applying the intensity ratio to the working curve. This step can also be simplified by setting up the calculating system shown in Figure 6-14. The percentage scale of working curve W for the element is projected to form scale D which is transferred as fixed scale D' (in place of scale A') to work with sliding scale B' from Figure 6-13.

The *index point (I.P.)* of a working curve, i.e., the element percentage for which the intensity ratio is 1.0, serves as a reference point in the same way as 1.0 on scale A' in Figure 6-13. Scales D' and B' in Figure 6-14 are shown set to read an element concentration value $E.P.$ of 0.1% for the transmission readings 65 and 20 of the analytical line $A.L.$ and standard line $S.L.$, respectively.

For a parallel working-curve shift, only the index point of scale D' has to be relocated but if the curve rotates, the scale must be completely reconstructed.

Calculators are available with a drum on which the D' scales for a large number of elements can be mounted parallel to one another. Then the drum is rotated to bring any desired scale adjacent to scale B'.

Semiquantitative analysis with a calibrated master-spectrum film

A sample in dry, powdered form can be semiquantitatively analyzed by comparing its spectrum with a series of calibrated master spectra. To avoid a crowded spectrogram, a master should include not more than fifteen elements, none of which has a line that will interfere with the line chosen to identify any of the other elements. For example, if zinc is to be identified by its 3302.6 A line, sodium should not be included in the same master spectrum because of its line at 3302.3 A.

A calibrated master film can be made as follows.

An identification line and a confirming line are chosen for each element to be included and the form in which each element will be represented in a series of standard mixtures is decided on. High-purity oxides, carbonates, or sulfates are preferred, if available.

The amount of each compound required to make a mixture with graphite that contains 1% of each element is calculated.

Examples

What weight of iron oxide, Fe_2O_3, must be present in 10 grams of a mixture that includes 1% of iron? The molecular weight of Fe_2O_3 is 159.70 ($2 \times 55.85 + 3 \times 16 = 159.70$). The mixture contains 0.1 gram of iron. (1% of $10 = 0.1$). Since the weight ratio of Fe_2O_3 to 2Fe is 159.70/ 2×55.85, the weight of iron oxide equivalent to 0.1 gram of iron is 0.143 gram ($159.70 \times 0.1 / 2 \times 55.85 = 0.143$).

What weight of calcium carbonate, $CaCO_3$ is equivalent to 0.1 gram of Ca? The molecular weight of $CaCO_3$ is 100.09 ($40.08 + 12.01 + 3 \times 16 = 100.09$). The weight of calcium carbonate equivalent to 0.1 gram of calcium is 0.25 gram. ($100 \times 0.1 / 40.08 = 0.25$).

Table 6-5 lists the data required to produce a calibrated master film for fifteen elements.

TABLE 6—5

Data required to produce a calibrated master film for fifteen elements

Element	Compound	Identifica- tion line (A)	Confirming line (A)	Grams of compound for 0.1 gram of element
Mn	MnO	2576.1	2933.1	0.129
Fe	Fe_2O_3	3020.6	2599.4	0.143
Ca	$CaCO_3$	4226.7	3179.3	0.250
Na	Na_2SO_4	3302.3	5890.0*	0.309
Ni	NiO	3414.8	3050.8	0.127
Si	SiO_2	2881.6	2516.1	0.214
Al	Al_2O_3	3082.2	3092.7	0.189
Cr	Cr_2O_3	4254.3	4274.8	0.146
Ti	TiO_2	3349.0	3341.9	0.167
B	H_3BO_3	2496.8	2497.7	0.572
Cu	CuO	3274.0	3247.5	0.125
Mg	MgO	2852.1	2795.5	0.156
P	$NH_4H_2PO_4$	2535.7	2553.3	0.371
Pb	PbO	2833.1	2663.2	0.108
Sn	SnO_2	2840.0	3175.0	0.127

*Cannot be detected on S.A. No. 3 film.

Procedure

The calculated weight of each compound is mixed thoroughly with 6.86 grams of spectrographic-grade graphite powder. The concentration of each element in the resulting mixture is 1%. This is the basic standard from which a series of more dilute ones are prepared as follows:

0.3% standard — mix 3.00 grams of 1% standard with 7.00 grams of graphite.

0.1% standard — mix 3.33 grams of 0.3% standard with 6.66 grams of graphite.

0.03% standard — mix 3.00 grams of 0.1% standard with 7.00 grams of graphite.

0.01% standard — mix 3.33 grams of 0.03% standard with 6.66 grams of graphite.

0.003% standard — mix 3.00 grams of 0.01% standard with 7.00 grams of graphite.

0.001% standard — mix 3.33 grams of 0.003% standard with 6.66 grams of graphite.

The standard mixtures are stored in tightly stoppered containers. Standards for any other desired concentration ranges can be prepared from the 1% standard.

The spectrum of a sample of each mixture is recorded on a single strip of S.A. No. 3 film, using a Hartmann diaphragm or a film mask as shown in Figure 6-15. Excitation-source conditions (a d-c arc is best), exposure time, etc., are adjusted to give the best possible results with the spectrographic equipment available.

For each spectrogram, a 20-milligram sample of standard is packed into an undercut electrode and arced against a solid counterelectrode. The gap between the electrode tips should be maintained at about 6 millimeters during arcing and kept centered on the spectrograph slit. These adjustments can be made by viewing an image of the arc as described in Chapter 5. The sample electrode should be positive if a d-c excitation source is used. An iron spectrum should also be included on the film.

After a film has been developed, the spectra are examined with a magnifying lens or on a projection screen and the element-identification lines are located and labeled on the film with a fine-pointed needle.

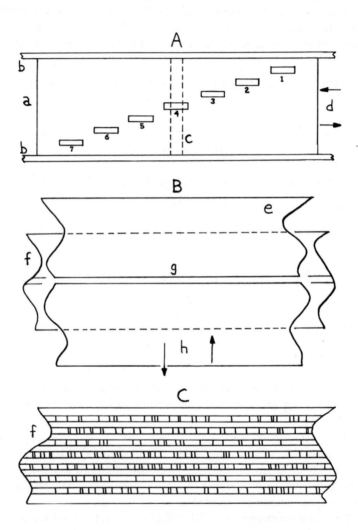

Figure 6-15. CALIBRATED MASTER FILM

A – *Preparation of master spectra with a Hartmann diaphragm: a* – diaphragm in front of the spectrograph slit; *b* – diaphragm tracks; *c* – spectrograph slit; *d* – indicates that the diaphragm can be moved horizontally; 1 to 7 – diaphragm slots.
B – *Preparation of master spectra with a film mask: e* – mask in front of the film; *f* – film; *g* – slot in the mask; *h* – indicates that the film (camera) can be moved vertically.
C – *Appearance of master film: f* — section of film with seven standard spectra.

Sample analysis

The sample is powered and dried, 0.1 gram is diluted with 0.9 gram of graphite powder, and 20 milligrams of the mixture are arced under the same conditions as were the standards. If several samples are to be analyzed, the spectra of as many as possible should be recorded on the same film. The sample film should also include an iron spectrum.

The calibration and sample films are viewed simultaneously on the screen of a film viewer (see Figure 3-15) or microphotometer, or with an overhead projector. They are aligned in accordance with their iron spectra, readily identifiable lines, or the cyanogen bands. Concentration estimates are made by comparing the blackness of element-identification lines in the sample with those of the standard spectra.

If, for example, the density of the copper line in a sample falls between that of the copper lines of the 0.003 and 0.01% standards, the concentration of the element is reported to be between 0.03 and 0.1% since the original sample was diluted with graphite tenfold. For elements whose concentration is greater than 10%, the sample must be diluted in the ratio of 1:100.

In addition to graphite, many other substances may be used as standard matrix materials and sample diluents. Common ones are SiO_2, Al_2O_3, $CaCO_3$, and mixtures of these compounds.

If a microphotometer is available, more-accurate semiquantitative results can be obtained from transmission readings than are possible by visual estimates of line blackness. An elaborate system of analysis that can be applied to samples in many different matrices has been developed. (See reference 3 at the end of this chapter.)

Qualitative analysis

Qualitative analysis can be made more useful than merely element identification if the lowest concentration of an element that can be detected spectroscopically has been determined previously. The *detection limit* is the approximate concentration of an element that produces a just-perceptible line under a given set of analytical conditions. In many cases, with suitable comparison standards, visual analysis with a spectroscope can be made semiquantitative.

If the background is visible on a spectrogram, additional exposure will not bring out lines not already present because the background intensity will also increase. In other words, a just-visible background insures that all of the lines that can be detected under the prevailing conditions are also visible.

Qualitative analysis should be performed with a narrow slit which produces high resolution and makes possible the separation and identification of adjacent lines that might not be resolved at a greater slit width that is more suitable for quantitative analysis.

The results of a qualitative or semiquantitative analysis may furnish all the necessary information about the composition of a sample or they may be used to indicate those elements that require determination by more-exact spectrographic or chemical quantitative methods.

REFERENCES

(1)   *Spectrochemical Procedures,* C. E. Harvey, Applied Research Laboratories, Glendale, Calif. (1950). Extensive coverage of all phases of spectrographic analysis.

(2)   "Techniques of Quantitative Spectrographic Analysis," J. R. Churchill. *Industrial & Engineering Chemistry,* analytical edition, vol. 16, p. 653 (1944). Intensive discussion of practical factors involved in quantitative analysis.

(3)   *Semiquantitative Spectrochemistry,* C. E. Harvey. Applied Research Laboratories, Glendale, Calif. (1964). Techniques of semiquantitative analysis, includes also extensive line and interference tables and matrix factors.

(4)   *Principles and Practice of Spectrochemical Analysis,* N. H. Nachtrieb, McGraw-Hill, New York City (1950). Chapter 5, conversion of line transmission readings to element-concentration values.

(5)   *Manual of Analytical Procedures,* Applied Research Laboratories, Glendale, Calif. Intended primarily for use with ARL Spectrographic Analyzer but most of the information is applicable to any spectrograph.

(6)   *Methods for Emission Spectrochemical Analysis,* any edition, American Society for Testing Materials, Philadelphia, Pa.

(7)   *Optical Methods of Chemical Analysis,* T. R. Gibb, McGraw-Hill, New York City (1942) Chapter 1.

(8)   *Analytical Chemistry,* vol. 1, "Qualitative Analysis," F. P. Treadwell and W. T. Hall, John Wiley, New York City (1932). Good discussion of visual analysis with the spectroscope; pages 122-132.

CHAPTER 7

Auxiliary analytical techniques

Sampling

Metals

Homogeneous metal, such as tubes, rods, sheets, turnings, drillings, pigs, and castings, can be analyzed directly. Soft metals, such as high-purity copper and solders, are easiest to sample with a coarse file or hacksaw, whereas harder metals must be drilled, sheared, sawed, or machined.

When it is not feasible to sort out representative ingredients from a mixture, for example, drillings from a mixture of different types of alloys, the entire lot may be melted and the resulting metal button or ingot sampled. High-temperature melting equipment is required for metals other than the easily fusible ones, such as lead and tin alloys. Metallurgical or foundry-practice references should be consulted for details.

Filings, sawings, light turnings, etc., should be briquetted to avoid losses due to gas currents in the arc while the sample is burning. Hydraulic briquetting presses are available but they are quite expensive. Figure 7-1 shows a simple, easily constructed press that is adequate in many cases.

Sample *a* is packed into heavy-walled steel tube *b* after end plug *c* has been inserted. Plunger *d* is pushed down as far as possible and the press is placed between jaws *e* of a vice which is then closed to compress the metal. After removing the end plug, the briquet is pushed out.

Nonmetallics

Nonmetallic materials, for example, rocks, glass, cement, and mineral crystals, should be crushed, ground, and thoroughly mixed before a sample is taken. This is usually done with a mortar and pestle which, if they are softer than the material being processed, may contaminate the

95

sample. Because of their greater hardness, agate or hardened-steel grinding tools are preferable to those made of glass, iron, or porcelain. Large specimens must first be broken down with a rock crusher or on a steel plate with a hammer.

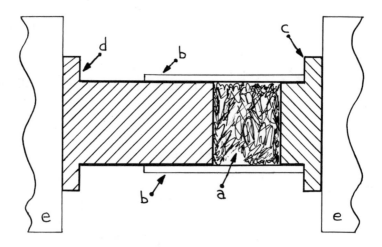

Figure 7-1. BRIQUETTING PRESS

a — sample; *b* — heavy-walled steel tube; diameter ½ inch, length 1 inch; *c* — end plug (steel); *d* — plunger (steel); *e* — vice jaws.

Wet and carbonate samples

Materials containing water or organic liquids, hydrated crystals, etc., should be predried to avoid sample losses during arcing due to the explosive formation of steam or other vapors. Carbonate samples should be finely ground and decomposed in a furnace to release their carbon dioxide.

Sample concentration

Dilute solutions are concentrated by heating or by allowing the solvent to evaporate. When only a small volume remains, the sample can be analyzed directly by a solution excitation method or taken up with a piece of filter paper which is dried at 100°C in a crucible, then wet with alcohol, charred with a low Bunsen flame, and finally burned completely at a higher temperature or ignited in a muffle furnace. The residue, which should be handled carefully to prevent losses, is mixed with graphite and arced.

Organic materials, such as plant and animal tissues, can be treated by a similar procedure, called *dry ashing*. The sample, in a crucible or evaporating dish, is first dehydrated, then charred at a higher temperature, and finally baked in a muffle furnace until only metal oxides or sulfates remain. The loss of volatile metals, such as arsenic and mercury, should be kept in mind when a sample is dry ashed.

Air samples

Air can be examined for fine particles of metals or their compounds by pulling a sample through a highly retentive filter paper, Millipore filters being best for this purpose. The paper can be burned directly in the excitation source, or the trapped particles can be dissolved by decomposing the filter in a 1:1 solution of 50% hydrochloric and nitric acids.

Chemical pretreatment of samples

Many substances must be chemically treated before being analyzed to eliminate the unwanted bulk of the sample, concentrate the elements of interest, or separate one or more metals from others. Separations are worthwhile when a matrix element has a complex spectrum that interferes with the detection of others or when analysis for only one or of a few elements is required.

Solution methods

Wet ashing

This process consists of dissolving an organic or biological sample in a mixture of sulfuric and nitric acids to reduce it to a solution that contains only inorganic compounds.

Inorganic materials, such as ceramics, slags, and minerals, may also be dissolved, but the choice of acids depends on the nature of the sample. Samples containing metals of the gold or platinum group, for example, must be dissolved with *aqua regia,* a mixture of hydrochloric and nitric acids, titanium-bearing substances require sulfuric acid, and those with high silica content must be attacked with a mixture of hydrofluoric and sulfuric acids.

Fusion

Many materials are best broken down by heating them in a metal crucible together with fluxes, such as sodium carbonate, potassium bisulfate, or borax, until the mixture melts. This converts the metals in the sample to compounds that are soluble in hydrochloric acid.

Separation methods

Sulfide precipitation

Group seperations of dissolved metals can be made by precipitating them as sulfides with hydrogen sulfide at controlled pH levels. For example, As, Mo, Ag, Cu, Sb, Bi, Hg, Au, Pt, Sn, Cd, and Pb are precipitated by H_2S at an approximate pH level of 3, whereas Fe, Zn, Co, Cr, Al, Ti, Ni, and the alkali and alkaline-earth metals are not.

Precipitation with ammonium hydroxide

Precipitation of metals from solution as hydroxides with ammonium hydroxide is even less selective than sulfide precipitation but the two used together or in combination with other methods may be very useful.

Precipitation with sodium hydroxide

Precipitation with sodium hydroxide may be used to separate amphoteric elements, such as Ga, Al, Be, Zn, Mo, Sn, Pb, V, Cr, and W, the hydroxides of which are soluble in strong alkali solutions, from Fe, Ti, Zr, In, Sc, Y, Th, and the rare earth elements whose hydroxides are insoluble in sodium hydroxide.

Ether extraction

The elements Fe, Tl, Ga, Au, and Mo can be extracted almost completely from six-molar hydrochloric acid solution with diethyl or isopropyl ether. This procedure is especially suitable for the removal of iron from geological samples and from iron and steel alloys. The elimination of iron, a prolific source of spectral lines, makes the detection of other elements in a sample much easier.

Extraction and precipitation with other organic reagents

Dithizone (diphenylthiocarbazone) in carbon tetrachloride or chloroform solution extracts Mn, Fe, Co, Ni, Cu, Zn, Pd, Ag, Cd, In, Sn, Te, Pt, Au, Hg, Tl, Pb, and Bi from aqueous solution by complex formation. Considerable selectivity is possible by pH control and the simultaneous use of masking agents, such as cyanide, thiocyanide, thiosulfate, and EDTA (ethylene diamine tetraacetic acid).

Other important extractants and precipitants are 8-quinolinol (8-hydroxy-quinoline), acetylacetone, cupferron (the ammonium salt of nitrosophenylhydroxylamine), so called because it was originally used to separate copper and iron from other elements, and methyl isobutyl ketone.

Mercury-cathode separation

This is an electrochemical method by which metals below Zn in the electromotive series of the elements are separated from others higher in the series. The sample solution is electrolyzed in the apparatus shown in Figure 7-2 with the mercury as the cathode. Bi, Co, Cu, Cr, Fe, Mo, Ni,

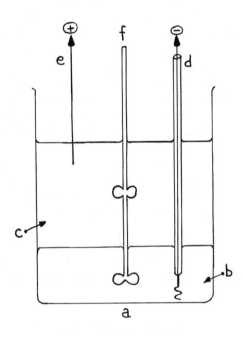

Figure 7-2. MERCURY-CATHODE ELECTROLYZER

a — heavy-walled glass or plastic container; *b* — mercury; *c* — sample solution; *d* — platinum cathode wire sealed in a glass tube to the negative terminal of a variable 6-volt d-c source; *e* — platinum anode wire to the positive terminal of the power source; *f* — motor-driven stirrer.

Ag, and Sn, among others, are deposited in the mercury, whereas the alkali, alkaline-earth, and rare-earth metals, and Al, Be, Mg, V, Ti, Zr, U, P, and As remain in the solution.

Chemical-separation methods, even though their selectivity leaves much to be desired, are useful because most samples contain only a relatively small number of elements and also because partial separations are often acceptable in spectrochemical work. For example, removal of 95% of the iron from a stainless-steel sample may sufficiently simplify its spectrum to allow easy detection of the alloying elements.

Suppression of cyanogen (CN) bands in the direct-current arc

Sensitive lines of several elements, especially of the rare earths, cannot be detected when graphite electrodes are used because of the CN bands that are formed in the 3500 to 4200 A region (see Figure 4-1). This interference can be eliminated by surrounding the arc with an atmosphere of steam, oxygen, helium, or other gases which exclude air nitrogen, but the technique is complicated and expensive.

Other solutions of the problem, such as working with lines outside the region of interference, the use of a spark source instead of an arc, and substituting electrodes of copper, silver, or aluminum for graphite, result in reduced analytical sensitivity.

Another approach involves the use of a mixture of graphite powder and a salt, the so-called *buffer,* as a sample diluent. Lithium carbonate is often used as a buffer. Lithium atoms are preferentially excited because of their low excitation potential which results in greatly reduced intensity of the CN bands so that analytical lines in those regions can be identified. Lithium carbonate reduces line sensitivity throughout the spectrum by varying degrees but band elimination makes this a worthwhile compromise. This difficulty can be partially overcome by arcing a separate sample without the buffer and using this spectrogram for lines outside the band regions.

The most effective lithium carbonate-to-graphite ratio, which typically varies from 1:2 to 1:10, must be determined by trial and error for each sample. The best buffer-to-sample ratio must also be determined experimentally.

Sample contamination

The apparatus and chemicals used in sample preparation may be unsuspected sources of contamination in spectrochemical analysis. The pulverizing equipment should be cleaned thoroughly after each use to prevent carryover of impurities to the next sample. The efficiency of decontamination can be checked by comparing the spectrum of a substance, such as high-purity silica, with that of a sample of the same substance after it has been pulverized in the supposedly clean equipment.

Pretreatment chemicals, such as acids, fluxes, graphite powder, and lithium carbonate, should be spectrographically analyzed if there is any doubt as to their purity. Foreign impurities are a problem only when they include, or interfere with, elements of interest in the sample. Otherwise, having been detected, their lines in the sample spectrum can usually be ignored.

It is permissible to cut a new tip on a graphite counterelectrode and reuse it if the same type of material is repeatedly analyzed. When electrodes are reused for different types of samples impurities from a previous sample can be carried over on the rod or picked up from the electrode-tip shaper.

Manufacturers of graphite electrodes, which are available in routine- and ultrahigh-purity grades, include an impurity analysis with each lot sold. Electrode rods may be used as a source of graphite powder.

Applications of spectrum excitation sources

Direct-current arc

The d-c arc is a widely used source for both qualitative and quantitative work. Best results are usually obtained with positive sample-electrode polarity at currents of 5 to 15 amperes. The arc cannot be maintained if the current is too low and flares if it is too high.

Samples are fused by the intense heat of the d-c arc and the elements present tend to volatilize or distill selectively, those with lower boiling points leaving the electrode crater first. Incomplete vaporization of a sample may lead to erroneous results if the more-refractory elements are left behind in the electrode crater.

Samples often have to be arced for several minutes, with periodic adjustment of the electrode gap, to insure complete vaporization, during which time, the large amount of graphite that is burned produces a heavy background throughout the spectrum as well as intense cyanogen bands. This can be alleviated by the use of a rotating intensity-control sector which regularly samples the light during the arcing period but allows only a fraction of the total amount to enter the spectrograph.

A sample can be arced in two stages to produce two separate spectra. Lines of the more-volatile elements appear in the first one, whereas higher-boiling elements are detected in the second spectrum.

The addition of powdered graphite to a sample usually makes the arc burn more smoothly and often reduces fractional volatilization. Fluxing compounds, such as Na_2CO_3, $NaCl$, SiO_2, and borax are also used for this purpose.

Ammonium chloride and sulfate, which vaporize when heated, are sometimes added to a sample to assist in blowing it out of the electrode crater and up into the arc. This technique is especially useful when hard-to-volatilize elements are present.

Certain elements, for example, aluminum, form oxide beads which tend to pop out of the electrode crater. This can be overcome by mixing the sample with a fluxing agent.

Metal samples can be analyzed with the d-c arc shown in Figure 5-2c. This method, in which the sample acts as a self-electrode, is used primarily for the identification of alloys.

Low-voltage a-c arc (115 volts)

The construction and use of an excitation source of this type is discussed in detail in Appendix B. It is essentially a qualitative source but may also be used for rough quantitative work.

Oxyhydrogen solution source

This source is also discussed in Appendix B.

High-voltage a-c arc; high-voltage interrupted d-c arc; high-voltage spark

These sources are especially suitable for the routine quantitative analysis of metals, with the sample acting a self-electrode as shown in Figure 5-2d or as in Figure 5-2a when the sample is rod shaped. The spark source is also used for solution work by the porous-cup method (Figure 5-3i) or the rotating-disc technique (Figure 5-2e).

Flame excitation sources

Flame sources, even the hotter ones, such as air/acetylene, have limited use with an ordinary spectrograph because of their relatively low sensitivity. Nevertheless, about seventy metals can be detected if present in large-enough amounts and some elements, notably the alkali and alkaline-earth metals, at very low concentrations because of their low excitation potentials.

Solutions are introduced into a flame with an atomizer. To obtain reproducible results, specially designed apparatus that premixes the sample with air and fuel gas must be used. Burners must be cleaned regularly and the burner top must be constructed of metal that does not corrode under the combined effect of high temperature and sample solution.

The sample solution can be absorbed in a piece of filter paper which is then dried, tightly rolled up, and burned. The procedure for introducing the paper into the flame must be reproducible.

Flame spectra, in most cases, have the advantage of extreme simplicity. Many of the lines that are excited in an electrical source and that might cause interference do not appear in a flame spectrum.

Sample-electrode techniques

Liquid samples

The sample can be transferred dropwise to a cup or crater-type electrode that contains graphite powder. An electrode with a rounded tip can be dipped into the sample solution and, after the solvent has evaporated, the residue arced.

Surface tension that prevents uniform spreading of a liquid over a graphite surface can be overcome by precoating the electrode tip with a film of glycerin or concentrated sugar solution if the sample is dissolved in water or with a heavy alcohol, such as butyl alcohol, in the case of organic solvent.

Finely divided substances

Samples of this type, after having been mixed with the required additives and perhaps a few drops of glycerin or sugar solution, can be briquetted in a small-diameter press to prepare pellets that will fit in the electrode crater.

Miscellaneous hints

Some experimentation is usually required to determine the correct exposure time, electrical conditions, etc., for obtaining a satisfactory spectrogram for an unknown sample. If there is plenty of material, the analysis can be repeated several times if necessary but when only a small amount is available, the spectrographer must, depending on the capabilities of his instrument, perform the analysis under average conditions that he knows from experience will give satisfactory results.

It is advisable to install an exhaust hood with a good draft over the excitation-source stand to avoid inhalation of cyanogen or fumes from toxic metals, such as mercury, beryllium, cadmium, lead, and zinc. If this is not possible, the laboratory should at least be well ventilated.

REFERENCES

(1) *Analytical Chemistry,* vol. 1., 8th edition. F. P. Treadwell and W. T. Hall. John Wiley, New York City (1932). Chapter 4, visual spectroscopic analysis.

(2) *Applied Inorganic Analysis,* 2nd edition, G. E. F. Lundell, H. A. Bright, and J. I. Hoffman, John Wiley, New York City (1953). Chemical methods of metal analysis with special emphasis on geological materials.

(3)   *Solvent Extraction in Analytical Chemistry,* G. H. Morrison and H. Freiser, John Wiley, New York City (1957).

(4)   *Outlines of Methods of Chemical Analysis,* G.E. F. Lundell and J. I. Hoffman. John Wiley, New York City (1938). Separation methods for metals.

(5)   *Advanced Quantitative Analysis,* H. H. Willard and H. E. Diehl, D. Van Nostrand, New York City (1943). Sampling and analytical techniques.

(6)   *Scott's Standard Methods of Chemical Analysis,* Volumes 1 and 2, 5th edition, N. H. Furman, editor, D. Van Nostrand, New York City (1939).

(7)   *Kodak Materials for Emission Spectroscopy,* Eastman Kodak Pamphlet P-10, 2nd edition, Eastman Kodak Co., Rochester, N. Y.

(8)   *Methods for Emission Spectrochemical Analysis,* periodic editions, American Society for Testing Materials, Philadelphia, Pa.

(9)   *Spectrochemical Analysis,* 2nd edition L. H. Aherns and S. R. Taylor, Addison-Wesley Publishing Co., Reading, Mass. (1961). Analysis of geological materials by direct current arc excitation.

(10) *Manual of Analytical Procedures,* Applied Research Laboratories, Glendale, Ca. (1964). Condensed practical spectrochemical procedures.

(11) *Spectrochemical Procedures,* C. E. Harvey, Applied Research Laboratories, Glendale, Ca. (1950). Covers all phases of spectrographic analysis.

(12) *Optical Methods of Chemical Analysis,* T. P. Gibb, McGraw-Hill, New York City (1942). Chapter 1, spectrochemical analysis.

(13) *Spectroscopic Tricks,* L. May, Plenum Publishers, New York City vol. 1. (1967), vol. 2. 1972. Collection of miscellaneous techniques for spectrographic analysis.

(14) *Chemical Analysis by Flame Photometry,* R. Herrmann, and C.T.J. Alkemade, Chemical Analysis Monograph, Vol. 14, Interscience Publishers, New York City (1963).

(15) Millipore Technical Manuals ADM-30 and ADM-70, Millipore Corp., Bedford, Mass. Techniques for using Millipore filters for collecting particulates from air, gas, and liquid samples.

(16) Handbook of Analytical Chemistry, L. Meites, editor, McGraw-Hill, New York City (1962). Section on flame analysis by P. T. Gilbert.

(17) *Handbook of Chemistry and Physics,* any recent edition, Chemical Rubber Publishing Co., Cleveland, Ohio. Section E, flame spectra of the elements.

CHAPTER 8

Applications of emission spectroscopy in chemical analysis

The following examples are indicative of the wide variety of substances that can be analyzed for metallic elements by emission spectroscopy.

Geological substances

The earth's crust, our source of metals, consists largely of rocks which are composed of minerals. Most rocks contain quartz (silica) and combinations of silica and aluminum, aluminum silicates. Rocks are rarely pure silica or aluminum silicates but include varying amounts of metals other than aluminum, sometimes in native form, but usually as oxides, sulfides, sulfates, carbonates, and other compounds. This accounts for the complexity of geological samples. Emission spectroscopy is an unexcelled technique for a first look to determine their general composition.

Metallurgical samples

The spectrograph is routinely used in the manufacture of metal products, for the analysis of high-purity metals and alloys, and also of metal-industry wastes, such as furnace slags and mining residues. The spectroscope is in wide use for the sorting, verification, and identification of alloys by scrap-metal dealers and users of metals.

Biological samples

Animal tissues and fluids, such as blood, urine, saliva, bones, hair, and internal organs, as well as plant juices, seeds, fruit, roots, leaves, etc., can be analyzed spectrographically. They usually contain relatively high concentrations of sodium, potassium, calcium, iron, magnesium, and phosphorus and traces of cobalt, copper, zinc, manganese, nickel, silver, molybdenum, and many other metals at trace levels.

Foods

Dairy products, beverages, fats and oils, cereal products, fruits and vegetables, meats, fish, canned products, etc., are also analyzed by spectroscopy, not only for determining nutritional value but also for detecting possible harmful contaminants.

Chemical purity

Spectrographic analysis is often used to maintain the composition and impurity levels of chemicals and chemical products within specification limits. The efficiency of a step in a wet analysis can be checked with the spectrograph, for example, to determine the degree of contamination by occlusion that occurs during a precipitation.

Electroplating

Plating solutions require periodic analysis for major constituents, whose concentration determines operating efficiency, and for contaminants that may cause imperfect coatings, which can be readily performed spectrographically.

Glass, ceramics, cement

Glasses are essentially mixtures of metal silicates. Their properties, such as fusion temperature, resistance to thermal and mechanical shock, color, wavelength transmission, and refractive index are determined by the types and relative concentrations of metals in a glass mixture. Ceramics and construction cements are chemically similar to glass. Materials of this type are routinely analyzed by emission-spectrographic methods.

Petroleum products

Many petroleum products contain metals; for example, metal soaps are largely responsible for the lubricating properties of greases. The maintainence of large engines, such as those in trucks, airplanes, locomotives, and stationary power sources requires periodical analysis of the lubricating oil used for tiny metal particles from bearings, and piston and cylinder walls. The spectrograph is an efficient tool for such determinations.

Water

The discharge of metals into rivers, lakes, and the ocean from sewage and industrial and mining wastes requires constant monitoring as part of our water-pollution control program. This can be done spectrographically.

Air

The spectrograph is used for the determination of finely divided particles of toxic metals that are often present in air in dangerously high concentrations. For example, antiknock compounds in gasoline are the sources of lead, and other metals are constantly discharged into the atmosphere from the stacks of industrial plants and metal refineries.

Cosmetics

Cosmetic products frequently contain metals, such as iron, zinc, aluminum, mercury, calcium, magnesium, sodium, potassium, and bismuth, the concentration of which can be determined by spectroscopy and controlled to meet formula specifications.

Soils

The spectroscopic analysis of metals in soil is of interest to scientists in agriculture and agronomy.

Rare earths

Mixtures of rare-earth elements, which are extremely difficult to separate by wet chemical methods, are easily analyzed with the emission spectrograph.

Forensic medicine, toxicology, and law enforcement

The examination of human tissue for toxic metals in an autopsy or for research, and the analysis of pieces of evidence connected with law violations or crimes often require the services of a spectrographer.

REFERENCES

(1)   *Methods for Emission Spectrochemical Analysis,* American Society for Testing Materials, Phildelphia, Pa. Standard, tentative, and suggested methods for the analysis of metals in various types of materials; revised and expanded periodically.

(2)   "Analytical Applications of Emission Spectroscopy" *Industrial and Engineering Chemistry,* analytical edition, vol. 17, page 66, 1945.

TECHNICAL JOURNALS

Analytical Chemistry (especially pre-1960 editions).

Applied Spectroscopy. Issues for a 20- year period (from 1946 to 1966) include methods of analysis for practically all metals and many different types of alloys.

The design and construction of a concave-grating spectrograph

The construction of this spectrograph does not require any special skills or tools and, the grating and a quartz lens excepted, the required materials are available from hardware and lumber suppliers. The cost of the spectrograph, excluding that of the labor required for its construction, should not exceed $200 to $300, depending on the items already on hand. A comparable commercially manufactured instrument cannot be purchased for less than $3000.

The choice of an excitation source will depend on the type of work to be done with the spectrograph. The simplest electrical source that can be used is the 115-volt a-c arc unit described in Appendix B. The design of many other types, including direct-current, high-voltage alternating-current, and spark sources can be found in the spectrographic literature.

A spectrum-projection and line-identification system is also required. A densitometer, if available, can be used for quantitative work. The system described in Appendix C is satisfactory for semiquantitative and qualitative analysis and for obtaining quantitative results by the logarithmic-sector method.

Operating expenses for the spectrograph will include the cost of film, photographic processing chemicals, and graphite electrodes. The cost of the items required for sample preparation, chemicals, laboratory equipment, etc., will depend on the types of samples to be analyzed.

The spectrograph is designed for a 15,000-grooves-per-inch, 53-centimeter-focal-length grating and has a camera wavelength range of 2200 to 7200 A. With appropriate dimensional changes, any instrument-quality concave grating may be substituted.

Figure A-1 shows the outline of spectrograph housing *b*, with slit *d*, grating *f*, and camera *h* arranged on Rowland circle *a*. Light *c* from excitation source *m* strikes grating face *e* at an incident angle of 19° with respect to normal *g*.

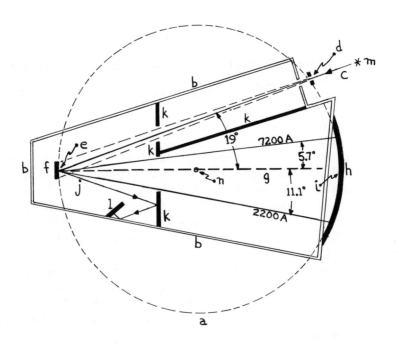

Figure A-1. GEOMETRICAL LAYOUT OF THE SPECTROGRAPH

a — Rowland circle (53-centimeter radius); *b* — spectrograph housing; *c* light from excitation source *m; d* — slit; *e* — grating face; *f* — grating support; *g* — normal; *h* — camera; *i* — film plane; *j* — zeroth order (reflected beam); *k* — stray-light baffles; *l* — reflected-beam trap; *m* — excitation source; *n* — center of Rowland circle.

From equation 2-6, the angles of diffraction for the extreme wavelengths of the camera range are calculated to be 5.7° and 11.1°.

$$m\,\lambda = a(\sin i + \sin d) \qquad \text{(Equation 2-6)}$$

The sum of these angles, 16.8°, determines the length of film *i* required to record the spectrum. From the geometry of a circle, the film length $= \pi r \theta / 90$, *r* being the radius of the Rowland circle and θ the angular spread between the ends of the spectrum.

Film length $= 3.14 \times 53 \times 16.8 / 90 = 31.1$ centimeters (12.25 inches) In practice, the camera is made long enough to allow for 2 inches of additional film length at each end. The reciprocal linear dispersion of the spectrograph will be 16.08 A per millimeter [(7200 — 2200) / 311 = 16.08].

Light baffles k absorb any stray reflected light to prevent fogging of the film and reflected-beam trap l absorbs the zeroth-order beam. The housing floor, which should be of good-quality 3/4-inch plywood, has the shape outlined by sides b and extends beyond the camera and slit as shown in Figure A-3.

Center n of the Rowland circle is located and the segments of the circle intercepted by the spectrograph are inscribed on the floor. This is done with a rigid-radius arm which can be made from a wood slat. Point e, the center of the grating face, is marked on the circle and normal line g, the diameter through point e, is drawn.

The 19° incident angle is carefully measured and constructed to locate the position of slit d and the 8.9° and 14.3° angles in Figure A-2 are drawn to indicate the limits of the camera on the circle.

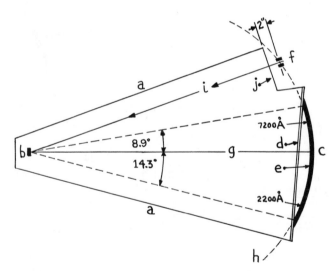

Figure A-2. DIMENSIONAL DETAILS OF THE CAMERA AND SLIT ON THE ROWLAND CIRCLE

a — spectrograph housing; b — grating; c — camera; d — camera support; e — film plane; f — slit; g — normal; h — Rowland circle; i — light from the excitation source; j — slit-assembly base.

The housing can then be completed as shown in Figure A-3. Plywood of 1/4-inch thickness is heavy enough for the sides a and aluminum sheet may be used for baffles e to keep down the weight of the instrument. Ports d, f, and g are 2 inches high while the height of camera port k is 1 inch.

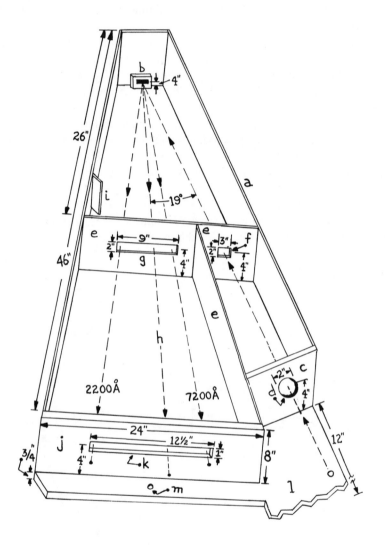

Figure A-3. LAYOUT OF THE SPECTROGRAPH HOUSING

a — housing wall (¼-inch plywood); *b* — grating; *c* — slit-assembly base (3/4-inch plywood) *d* — slit-tube port; *e* — stray-light baffles; *f* — entrance-light port; *g* — spectrum port in baffle; *h* — normal; *i* — reflected-beam trap; *j* — camera support; *k* — camera-support spectrum port; *l* — housing floor (3/4-inch plywood); *m* — hole for the camera-racking screw.

The grating, shown in Figure A-4A, a master grating replica, is supplied mounted on support block *a* and covered with mask *b*. Only the most-perfect area of the ruled surface, a rectangle *c* of 10 × 20 millimeters, is left exposed. The face of a diffraction grating should never be

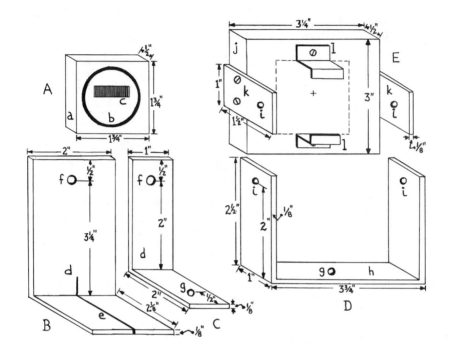

Figure A-4. GRATING-HOLDER COMPONENTS

A. Grating (Central Scientific Co. replica concave grating No. 86887-1, grade A, 15,000 grooves per inch, 53-centimeter focal length) *a* — grating support block; *b* — grating mask; *c* — exposed area of the grating (20×25 millimeters).
B. Support stand for the grating holder *d* — aluminum angle stock; *e* — center line; *f* — 1/4-inch-diameter hole for the z-axis rotation screw.
C. Component for the z-axis rotation adjustment; *d* — aluminum angle stock; *f* — 1/4-inch-diameter hole for the z-axis rotation screw; *g* — 1/4-inch-diameter hole for the y-axis rotation screw.
D. Component for the y-axis rotation adjustment *g* — 1/4-inch-diamter hole for the y-axis rotation screw; *h* — aluminum channel stock; *i* — 1/4-inch-diameter holes for the x-axis rotation screws.
E. Grating-support-block holder and x-axis rotation adjustment component; *i* — 1/4-inch-diameter holes for the x-axis rotation screws; *j* — wood or aluminum block; *k* — grating-holder arms; *l* — grating-support-block clamps.

touched with the fingers or exposed to chemical fumes that may corrode its reflective surface. The only cleaning that should be attempted is dust removal, if necessary, by gentle brushing with a fine camel-hair brush in the direction of the grooves (up and down) or by blowing on the grating air from a rubber bulb.

Center line *e* of the grating-holder support stand, shown in Figure A-4B, will coincide with the grating normal line when installed.

The grating is rotated about its z-axis by means of the component shown in Figure A-4C which is mounted on the grating-holder support stand with a 1/4-inch screw through holes *f*.

Figure A-4D shows the y-axis rotater that is mounted on the one illustrated in Figure A-4C with a 1/4-inch screw through holes *g*.

Grating support block *a* is held in place by clamps *l* on the support-

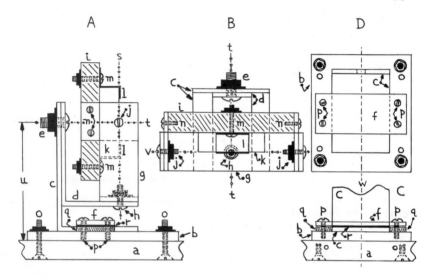

Figure A-5. ASSEMBLED GRATING HOLDER MOUNTED ON THE SPECTROGRAPH FLOOR

A. Side view: *a* — housing floor; *b* — aluminum plate; *c* — grating-holder support stand (Figure A-4B); *d* — z-axis rotation component (Figure A-4C); *e* — z-axis rotation screw, 1/4-inch (use lock washer); *f* — grating-holder-support-stand base clamp (1/8-inch aluminum or brass); *g* — y-axis rotation component (Figure A-4D); *h* — y-axis rotation screw, 1/4 inch (use lock washer); *i* — grating-support-block holder (Figure A-4E); *j* — x-axis rotation screw(s), 1/4 inch (use lock washers); *k* — grating support block, installed (Figure A-4A); *l* — grating-support-block clamps; *m* — grating-support-block clamp screws (use lock washers); *n* — grating-holder-arm screws; *o* — aluminum-plate holding screws (use lock washers); *p* — base-clamp holding screws; *q* — grating-holder-base guides(s); *r* — metal spacer; *s* — grating y-axis of rotation (vertically bisects and is tangent to the exposed area of the grating face); *t* — grating z-axis of rotation (coincides with the optical axis of the spectrograph; passes through the center of the exposed area of the grating face); *u* — distance from the optical axis to the housing floor (4 inches).

B. Top view: *c, d, e, g, h, i, j, k, l, m, n,* and *t* are the same as in Figure A-5A; *v* — grating x-axis of rotation (horizontally bisects and is tangent to the exposed area of the grating face).

C. Front view of the grating assembly mounted on the housing floor: *a, b, c, f, o, p, q,* and *r* are the same as in Figures A-5A and/or A-5B; *w* — center line of the grating-holder assembly.

D. Top view of the grating holder on the aluminum base plate: All letter designations are the same as in Figures A-5A, A-5B and/or A-5C.

block holder shown in Figure A-4E. The clamps should not touch the grating mask and their screws should be tightened only enough to keep the support block from moving. Excess pressure could distort the grating surface. The support-block holder is mounted on the grating-holder component in Figure A-4D with screws through holes i.

Figure A-5 illustrates the assembled grating holder on the spectrograph-housing floor. Figure A-5A is a side view that shows grating-holder-support stand c mounted on housing floor a. The z-axis rotation component d is mounted on support stand c with screw e and the y-axis rotation component g is mounted on component d with screw h. Grating-support-block holder i is mounted on component g with screw(s) j (see Figure A-5B).

The z-axis of rotation of the grating, line t, passes through the center of screw e and the center of the exposed area of the grating face. The y-axis of rotation, line s, passes through the center of screw h and vertically bisects and is tangent to the exposed area of the grating face.

The grating holder is mounted on aluminum plate b which, in turn, is mounted on housing floor a with screws o. The base of grating-holder-support stand c is maintained in place by grating-holder-base clamp f and guide(s) q (see Figure A-5C).

Figure A-5B is a top view of the assembled grating holder that shows the x-axis of rotation, line v passing through the centers of screws j. Line v horizontally bisects and is tangent to the exposed grating area.

Figure A-5C is a partial front view of Figure A-5A. It shows both guides q. When screws p are tightened, spacer r between clamp f and the base of support stand c assures that the grating holder will remain in its intended position.

Figure A-5D is a top view of the base of support stand c between aluminum plate b and support-stand-base clamp f.

Before the grating holder is assembled, all components are sprayed with flat black paint.

Figure A-6 shows camera base d against camera support a and between guides g. Black-velvet gasket h (about 1 inch wide) is glued to camera base d and, extending all the way around its perimeter, prevents outside light from leaking into the camera. The camera base should fit snugly between guides g and against sliding surface c but not so tightly that it cannot be pushed up and down easily.

Camera base d is supported by racking screw k which pushes against racking block i mounted on the camera base as shown. Screw k should be fitted with a steel disc (not shown) so that the end of the screw will not cut into the bottom of the block. The screw disc should be lubricated for smooth turning against the block. Screw k passes through a threaded hole in block *j* and a passing hole (*m* in Figure A-3) in housing-floor extension *b* and is turned by 3-inch-diameter wheel *l,* underneath the floor (see Figure A-12B). Clockwise rotation of the wheel raises the camera and pushing down on the top of its base *d* while turning the wheel counter-clockwise lowers it. Scale *m* is a film-position indicator.

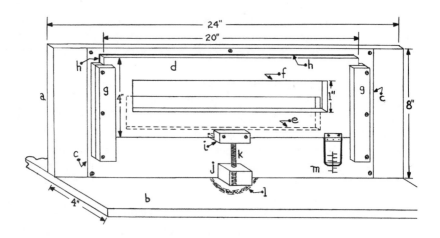

Figure A-6. MOUNTING DETAILS OF THE CAMERA BASE

a — camera support (see *j* in Figure A-3); *b* — spectrograph-housing floor extension; *c* — sliding surface for camera base d (1/16-inch aluminum sheet); *d* — camera base (1/8-inch aluminum plate); *e* — camera support spectrum port (see *k* in Figure A-3); *f* — camera base spectrum port; *g* — metal tracks; *h* — black-velvet gasket; *i* — steel camera-racking block; *j* — metal racking-screw block; *k* — steel racking screw; *l* — racking-screw control wheel of 3-inch diameter (see Figure A-12); *m* — film-position indicator (see Figure A-7).

Figure A-7 shows the film-position indicator in detail. Transparent plastic strip *a* is mounted (on camera base *d,* Figure A-6) with metal bracket *b* which is shaped so that when section *k* is riveted, or epoxy-glued to strip *a,* section *l* will fit against the bottom of the camera base and section *m* against the front of the base on which it is mounted with two screws over film-position indicator *m* (Figure A6). The plastic strip should clear camera support *a* by about 1 millimeter.

Film-position scales *d* and *e* are drawn on white cardboard strip *c.* Four-millimeter scale *d* allows four spectrograms to be photographed on a strip of film. The five-millimeter space *f* between adjacent steps provides for a one-millimeter space between spectrograms. Scale *e* is used for two-millimeter spectrograms, seven of which, also separated by one-millimeter spaces, can be photographed.

With plastic strip *a* mounted on camera base *d,* camera-support spectrum port *e* and camera-base spectrum port *f* (Figure A-6) are aligned and the location of scale-position indicator line *h* on the plastic strip is marked on camera support *a.* The plastic strip is then removed and and cardboard strip *c* is glued to the camera support with film-position reference line *i* in alignment with the line that has been drawn on the camera support. The plastic strip is then permanently screwed to the camera base.

If the dimensions in Figure A-7 are not reproduced exactly, the spectrograms will not be correctly positioned on the film. Strips *a* and *c*

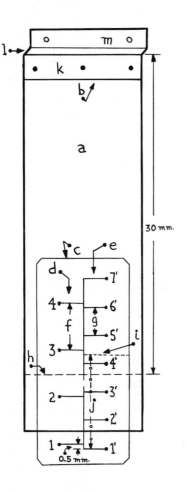

Figure A-7. FILM-POSITION INDICATOR

a — transparent plastic strip of 1/32-inch thickness; *b* — metal bracket for attaching plastic strip to camera base *d* (Figure A-6); *c* — white cardboard strip; *d* — film-position scale for 4-millimeter spectrograms; *e* — film-position scale for 2-millimeter spectrograms; *f* — spacing between lines on scale *d* (5 millimeters); *g* — spacing between lines on scale *e* (3 millimeters); *h* — scale-position indicator line on strip *a;* *i* — film-position reference line on strip *c;* *j* — distance between reference line *i* and bottom line of scale *e* (10 millimeters); *k* — section of bracket *b* attached to plastic strip *a*.; *l* — section of bracket *b* that fits under camera base *d* (Figure A-6); *m* — section of bracket *b* that is screwed to front side of camera base.

may have any convenient width since this dimension is not critical.

The screws that hold plastic strip *a* on the camera base can also be used to support a magnifying glass holder which should be centered on scale-position indicator line *h*. The lens will make it easier to align line *h* with the numbered lines on film-position scales *d* and *e*.

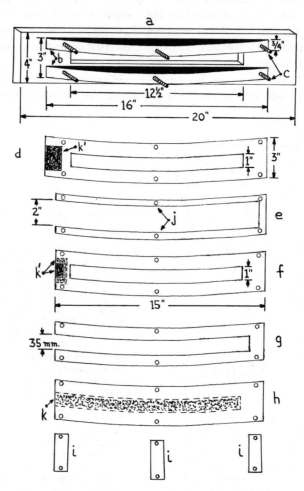

Figure A-8. CAMERA COMPONENTS

a − camera base (*d* in Figure A-6); *b* − camera arcs made of wood (*c* in Figure A-2); *c* − film-holder mounting screws; *d** − film-holder mask (1/16-inch thick); *e** − dark-slide track (3/64-inch thick), (see Figure A-9B); *f** − film mask (1/16-inch thick); *g** − film track (1/64-inch thick); *h** − film-holder back (1/16-inch thick); *i** − washers for mounting-screw nuts (1/16-inch thick); *j* − mounting-screw holes; *k* − black velvet (see Figure A-9A) film backing; *k'* − black-velvet light seals (see Figure A-9A).

---

*Flexible brass or aluminum sheet.

The camera components are shown in Figure A-8. The radius of curvature of arcs *b* is less than that of the Rowland circle by the total thickness of film-holder mask *d*, dark-slide track *e*, and film mask *f*, so that film track *g* will lie on the circle.

The length of mask *d* is the same as that of arcs *b*, whereas components *e*, *f*, *g*, and *h* are 1 inch shorter at the left end, so that the dark slide (see Figure A-9B) can be pulled out and reinserted when the film holder is mounted on the camera base. Parts *d*, *e*, *f*, *g*, and *h* are painted flat black.

Velvet strip *k* is cemented to the inside of film-holder back *h* to prevent scratching of the film as it is inserted and removed. The left end of velvet strip *k* and velvet tabs *k'* on both sides of film mask *f* and on the back of mask *d* are light seals for the film and dark-slide entrances (see Figure A-9A).

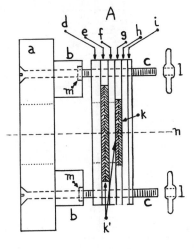

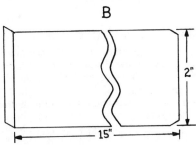

Figure A-9. ASSEMBLED CAMERA AND DARK SLIDE

A. Side view of the film holder mounted on the camera base: *a, b, c, d, e, f, g, h, i, k* are the same as in Figure A-8; *l* — wing nuts for the mounting screws; *m* — counter sunk nuts; *n* — optical axis of the spectrograph.

B. Dark slide: brass sheet stock of 1/32-inch thickness.

The film holder is assembled by covering both sides of *d*, *e*, *f*, *g*, and *h*, with the exception of the side of *d* that faces arcs *b* and the back (outside)

of *h*, with a thin layer of epoxy cement and mounting the five components on the arcs in the order shown in Figure A-9A, starting with mask
d. Rectangular washers *i* are cemented to film-holder back *h* and wing
nuts *l* are tightly screwed onto film-holder mounting screws *c*.

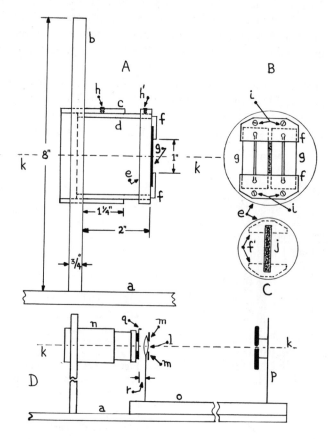

Figure A-10. SLIT ASSEMBLY AND OPTICAL BENCH

A. Side view of the mounted assembly: *a* — housing floor; *b* — slit-assembly base
(*j* in Figure A-2); *c* — fixed aluminum tube (2-inch outer diameter); *d* — adjustable-
position aluminum tube; *e* — slit-tube end cap; *f* — slit-blade holder; *g* — slit blades;
h, h' — setscrews; *k* — optical axis of the spectroscope.

B. Front view of the slit; *e* — slit-tube end cap; *f* — slit-blade holder; *g* — double-
edge razor blades; *i* — locking screws for the blades.

C. Slit-tube without blades or holders: *e* — cap; *f'* — blade-holder positions; *j* — light
slot (1 1/2 inches × 1/4 inch).

D. Optical-bench with accessories: *a* — housing floor; *k* — optical axis; *l* — source-
focussing quartz lens; *m* — lens mask (aperture: 1 × 1/4 inch); *n* — slit assembly;
o — optical-bench base; *p* — electrode support stand; *q* — slit shutter; *r* — about
1 inch (adjustable).

Velvet strip and tabs k and k', screws c, arcs b, screw holes j, and wing nuts l should be completely free of cement and none should obstruct tracks e and g. After about 24 hours, the cement will be dry and the film holder, whose curvature will conform to that of the arcs, may be removed.

Figure A-9A is a view of the left end of the camera with the film holder mounted on screws c but not in contact with arcs b as it should be. The dark slide, Figure A-9B, is inserted through the longer of the velvet seals and the film through the shorter one. One end of the dark slide is bent over, as shown, for convenient handling and the corners at the other end are trimmed so that it can easily be inserted into its track. Before a strip of film is loaded into the holder, its corners at one end should be similarly trimmed.

Figure A-10A shows the slit assembly mounted on its base b. Outer aluminum tube c is cemented into the slit port (d in Figure A-3). The exact position of sliding inner tube d, which is held in place by setscrew h, is determined when the slit is focussed.

The slit consists of a pair of double-edged razor blades g, shown in Figure A-10B, mounted in holder f on slit-tube end cap e. Figure A-10C shows slot j in the end cap which is covered by the razor blades, except the space between them (the slit opening).

The width of the opening, which must be centered on slot j, is adjusted by using a piece of paper of the desired thickness as a spacer. A spark-plug-gap spacer may also be used. Screws i (shown in Figure A-10B) are tightened just enough to hold the blades in position as excess pressure may distort the slit edges. Although the slit width can be reset, it is worthwhile to construct several slit caps with permanently mounted blades so that a selection of slit widths is available. Narrow slits, for example, with 10 and 20 micron openings, are used for qualitative work, whereas a wider one, such as 60 microns, is more suitable for quantitative analysis.

The inside of the slit assembly is sprayed with flat black paint, taking care not to obstruct the slit opening.

Figure A-10D shows a typical optical-bench arrangement. Slit shutter q, that keeps outside light from reaching the film when the spectrograph is not in operation, may be designed to slide up and down or pivot to one side when a spectrum is being photographed. Excitation-source focussing lens l should be stopped down with lens mask m having a rectangular aperture of about $1 \times 1/4$ inch.

Figure A-11 shows spectrum masking plate d mounted inside the spectrograph housing on camera support b. The height of mask slot e determines the spectrogram height on the film. As the camera is racked up or down, a new horizontal area of film is exposed to the slot opening. Masking plates for 2 and 4 millimeter spectrum-line heights should be available for different types of work. Spectrum-masking plates can easily be adapted for mounting film-calibration or line filters (see Chapter 6).

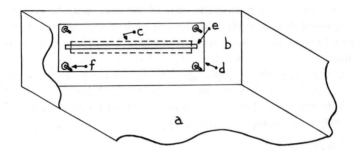

Figure A-11. SPECTRUM MASKING PLATE

a — housing floor; *b* — camera support; *c* — camera-support spectrum port; *d* – masking plate of 1/16-inch aluminum; *e* — mask slot (2 or 4 millimeters wide) *f* — mounting screws.

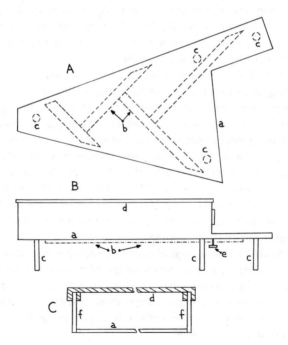

Figure A-12. VIEWS OF THE COMPLETED SPECTROGRAPH

A. The housing-floor supports: *a* — floor; *b* — location of floor braces (made of 3/4-inch thick wood); *c* — location of housing legs.
B. Side view of the assembled spectrograph: *a* — floor; *b* — floor braces; *c* — legs; *d* — top; *e* — camera-racking screw.
C. Cross-sectional view of the construction of the housing top: *a* — floor; *d* — top; *f* — walls.

Figure A-12A shows the location of housing legs *c* and floor braces *b* which maintain the optical alignment of the spectrograph.

Figure A-12B is a side view of the assembled spectrograph that shows braces *b* under housing floor *a*, and camera-racking wheel *e*. The construction of housing top *d* which is removable is shown in Figure A-12C. All interior parts of the spectrograph housing should be coated with flat black paint.

Alignment and focussing of the optical system

The time required to adjust the optical system can be greatly reduced by enlisting the help of an assistant.

A. Grating-rotation adjustment and focussing

The assembled grating holder is mounted on the housing floor as shown in Figure A-5. As closely as can be determined by eye, the grating face should be perpendicular to the normal, tangent to the Rowland circle, and its grooves should be vertical.

A strip of opaque 35-millimeter film is prepared by exposing a 6-inch length to bright light for a few minutes and developing it (see Chapter 5). Another 10-inch strip is placed directly into fixing solution without previous exposure or development and the resulting clear film is made translucent by rubbing it lightly with fine sandpaper. A centered horizontal line is drawn across the translucent film with a ball-point pen.

Temporary film tracks *b*, that coincide with the Rowland circle, are installed on the camera-base arcs *a* as shown in Figure A-13. A 6-inch strip of translucent film *c* is positioned as shown in Figure A-13A. The end cap of the slit assembly is removed (see Figure A-10) and replaced by a piece of cardboard with a $1/2 \times 1/8$ inch slot.

The room is darkened and a flashlight, with fresh batteries and its lens area masked to a 1 by 1/4 inch slot, is placed against the opening in the cardboard. If the grating is in at least fair alignment, a continuous spectrum will be seen on the film strip. If the spectrum does not appear, the x-, y-, and z-axis rotation adjustments are made to bring the spectrum onto the film and the spectrum is then positioned, horizontally with respect to center line *d* of the film, as shown in Figure A-13A. If the height of the spectrum turns out to be greater than the width of the film, the height of the slot in the cardboard slit-assembly cover will have to be reduced. Screws *e* and *j* in Figure A-5 are then tightened.

Then translucent film *c* is replaced by a 3-inch length of opaque film *h*, with a small hole *i* of about 1/2-millimeter diameter, as shown in Figure A-13B. Translucent film strip *j* is installed on the opposite side of line *g*. Hole *i* in the opaque film and point *k* on the translucent strip *j* must be exactly at the same distance from line *g* (4 inches is a convenient distance). A thin, flexible plastic ruler should be used to measure this distance.

Again in the dark, the flashlight is placed against hole i and film j is observed. If the y-axis adjustment of the grating is as it should be, which is unlikely, a spot of light (a zeroth-order reflection) will appear at point k. Rotation of the grating about axis s (see Figure A-5) will shift the spot to point k. Screw h in Figure A-5 is then tightened and the rotational adjustments of the grating are complete.

Translucent film j is replaced with an opaque strip, about 2 inches long, and it is moved to the left so that the reflected beam from the grating can be seen. A piece of thin, white paper, an inch or two behind the camera-film plane, will act as a projection screen on which the image of the grating will appear as a small rectangle.

The opaque film strip on the left side is slowly pushed to the right. As its edge cuts through the light beam, the image of the grating on the paper

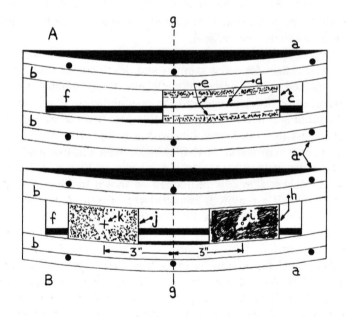

Figure A-13. FILM STRIPS ON THE CAMERA ARCS FOR GRATING ADJUSTMENTS

A. Film in place for y— and z-axis adjustment: a — camera arcs; b — temporary film tracks; c — translucent film strip; d — center line; e — height of the continuous spectrum on the film; f — camera-support spectrum port.

B. Film in place for x-axis rotation and focus adjustments: a — camera arcs; b — temporary film tracks; f — camera-support spectrum port; g — perpendicular to the grating normal; h — opaque film strip; i — pin hole; j — translucent film strip; k — location of the light-spot image.

will darken from left to right, in the *same* direction as the film is moving if the camera-film plane is *inside* the Rowland circle and in the *opposite* direction if it is *outside* the circle. This is the Foucault test for focussing a concave mirror.

Base-clamp holding screws *p* (see Figure A-5A) are loosened and the grating assembly is moved a few millimeters in the direction required to position the grating face on the Rowland circle with respect to the film plane. The Foucault test is repeated and further adjustments are made until the grating image on the paper darkens from top and bottom like an eye closing when the edge of the film intercepts the light beam. This indicates that the grating and film are on the Rowland circle. Screws *p* on the grating-holder base are tightened and temporary film tracks *b* on the camera arcs (Figure A-13) are removed.

B. Slit focussing

The slit-tube end cap is replaced by a piece of cardboard with a $1 \times 1/8$ inch slot and quartz lens *l*, with its mask *m*, is installed as shown in Figure A-10D. Electrode-support stand *p* on the optical bench is replaced by a light bulb behind a cardboard mask with a 3/4-inch hole. The center of the hole should be 4 inches from the spectrograph-housing floor and coincide with the optical axis of the instrument.

A piece of white cardboard (3×6 inches) with an outline of exposed grating area *c* (Figure A-4a) is placed against grating-support block *a* so that the outline coincides with area *c*. With the top of the spectrograph removed, the mask in front of the light bulb is positioned to focus the image of its hole on the grating outline. The mask-to-lens distance will be about 7 inches for a lens of 6-inch focal length.

The image of the mask hole will be about 6 inches high but that of a graphite source with a 3 to 4 millimeter gap between the electrodes will illuminate the grating approximately as shown in Figure 5-6.

The positions of the lens and light mask are marked on the optical-bench base and the light bulb is replaced by a mercury-vapor lamp. A small mercury bulb, such as is used to sterilize the air in a home clothes dryer, is satisfactory for this purpose. An end cap *e* with a 60-micron slit is installed on the slit-assembly tube (see Figure A-10).

The film holder is now tested for light leaks by inserting a strip of unexposed film and the dark slide and then turning on the darkroom light. (Enough film should be cut off from the roll so that about 2 inches will remain outside the film holder when the strip is inserted as far as it will go.) The film is developed after about an hour and, if it is not perfectly clear, the source of the light leaks in the film holder must be found and sealed.

The spectrograph, without a spectrum mask (see Figure A-11), with ports *e* and *f* in Figure A-6 in alignment, and with the loaded film holder in place, must also be tested for light leaks with the slit shutter closed and the dark slide pulled out. Again, after an hour of exposure to room light, the film holder is taken to the darkroom and the film is developed and examined. Leaks can be located with a 60-watt bulb inside the housing while the room is dark. This should be done as quickly as possible and with the grating shielded to avoid overheating.

Slit focussing involves photographing the mercury spectrum repeatedly, moving the slit between exposures until the best possible line definition is achieved. Type 103-0 or 103-F spectrographic film is required for this test (see Chapter 5), but ordinary panchromatic 35-millimeter film may also be used.

A spectrum-masking plate with a 4-millimeter slot (see Figure A-11) is installed, slit tube *d* (see Figure A-10) is positioned to set the slit on

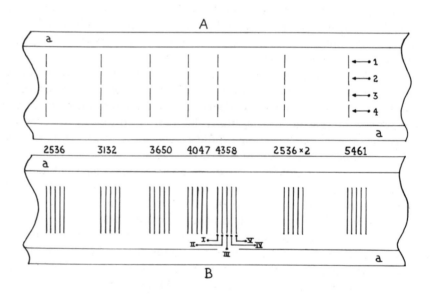

Figure A-14. FILMS FOR THE SLIT FOCUS TEST

A. Exposure-time spectra: 1 — 30-second exposure; 2 — 45-second exposure; 3 — 60-second exposure; 4 — 75-second exposure; a — sprocket-hole area of film.
B. Focus-position spectra: I — original-slit-position exposure; II — second-slit-position exposure; III — third-slit-position exposure; IV — fourth-slit-position exposure; V — fifth-slit-position exposure; a — sprocket-hole area of film.
The numbers between the films indicate the wavelengths of the lines. 2536 × 2 indicates a second-order line.

the Rowland circle as closely as can be estimated, the film holder is mounted, and the camera is racked for photographing spectrogram 1 (see Figure A-14A) by aligning spectrum-position indicator line h on transparent strip a with line 1 on film-position scale d (see Figure A-7).

The mercury lamp is turned on, the dark slide pulled out of the film holder, and the slit opened. After 30 seconds, the slit is closed and the camera racked up for the second exposure. Exposures 2, 3, and 4 should be made at 45, 60 and 75 seconds, respectively. Then the slit is closed, the dark slide reinserted, the mercury lamp turned off, and the film holder taken to the dark room.

The developed film is examined to determine the best exposure time for checking the line focus. Figure A-14A shows the major lines that will probably be seen. Horizontal streaks across the film are caused by dust particles in the slit which can be removed with a sharpened match stick.

The masking plate is now removed and a series of overlapping full-height spectrograms are photographed as shown in Figure A-14B, each at the previously determined exposure time. This is done with the camera at its center position.

Exposure 1 is made with the slit as set. Slit-assembly tube d is then moved exactly 2 millimeters closer to the mercury lamp, about 3 millimeters of film are pulled out of the camera, and spectrogram II is photographed. Tube d is moved 2 millimeters more in the same direction, another few millimeters of film are pulled out, and exposure III is made. Two more spectrograms, IV and V, are similarly photographed with the slit tube moved 2 and 4 millimeters, respectively, in the opposite direction from its original position. The slit should be closed between exposures while the slit tube is being moved and setscrew h (Figure A-10) should be retightened each time. A scale must be made that will indicate the exact position of tube d at each exposure.

Figure A-14B shows the developed focus-test film. The exposure-test film, Figure A-14A, is used as a guide for sorting out the lines that belong to each of the overlapping spectrograms on the focus film.

Final focussing of the slit is done by taking a second series of exposures (and more if necessary) on either side of the slit-tube position that showed the best focus in the first series. Perfectly focussed lines are sharply defined and have straight sides. Slightly out-of-focus lines have concave sides. Vertical misalignment of the slit with respect to the grating grooves (which is corrected by rotation of tube d) may be responsible for apparently out-of-focus lines. In cases of gross vertical misalignment, each line appears on the film as a group of vertically displaced lines.

The spectrograph is ready for operation after the electrode stand has been installed on the optical bench. Chapter 5 should be referred to before purchasing film.

The theoretical resolving power of this spectrograph in the first order is 12,000 (see Chapter 2). Assuming an actual resolution of 4000, the instrument will resolve lines 0.75 A apart in the 3000 A region, 1 A apart at 4000 A, and, at 5000 A, lines that differ in wavelength by 1.25 A can be distinguished. It should be kept in mind that the actual resolving power decreases with increasing slit width.

False lines, known as *Rowland ghosts,* which are due to grating imperfections, can be identified by their appearance in symmetrically spaced pairs on either side of intense true lines.

Spectrum excitation sources
(115-volt a-c)

A. Arc Source

The circuit diagram of this source, shown in Figure B-1, is similar to that built into the Vreeland spectroscope (see Chapter 3). The arc current is limited to approximately 10 amperes by parallel resistors *b* that can be constructed from nichrome resistance wire, such as that used in electrical

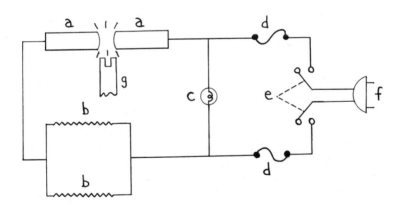

Figure B-1. 115-VOLT ALTERNATING CURRENT ARC SOURCE
a — graphite electrodes; *b* — nichrome-wire resistors (about 1000 watts each); *c* — 25-watt light bulb; *d* — 15-ampere fuse; *e* — heavy-duty double-pole single-throw switch; *f* — plug to a 115-volt a-c outlet; *g* — graphite or ceramic sample holder.

appliances. Coiled nichrome wire wound on a ceramic form that screws into a standard light-bulb socket is an easily available hardware item that is especially convenient for this purpose. Toasters, clothes irons, room heaters, etc., can also be used as ballast resistors.

All connections should be tight and No. 14 B & S gauge or thicker copper connecting wire should be used to avoid overheating.

When switch e is closed, safety bulb c lights up. This indicates voltage in the circuit even though the arc may not be in operation. The arc is started by bringing electrodes a together and then separating them by about 1/4 inch. This can be safely done while wearing a leather glove or with an insulated tool; only *one* hand should be used.

The electrode-support system must insulate the arc electrodes from the tabletop or other surface on which the spectroscope is standing. The surface itself must be a nonconductor or covered with a heat-resistant, nonconducting material, such as Transite.

This excitation source and the one shown in Figure B-2, both of which receive their power from the supply line without an intervening isolation transformer (the autotransformer in Figure B-2 is *not* an isolation transformer), can be a safety hazard because of the possibility of an accidental short circuit to ground through the operator. For this reason, the laboratory floor should be absolutely dry. A rubber floor mat is a good additional safety measure.

Since pure graphite will not maintain a 115-volt a-c arc, special electrodes, available from Spectrex Corp. (see Chapter 3), must be used. They carry a small amount of sodium chloride whose lines should be noted before a sample is introduced into the arc. The sodium doublet in the spectrum of the electrodes can be used as a wavelength reference point.

After the arc has been struck, sample container g, which may be a a cratertype graphite electrode or a ceramic boat, as shown in Figure 5-2b, is moved up close to the electrode gap where the heat from the arc can vaporize the sample. It should be noted that g is *not* in the electrical circuit. If more than about 1 minute of continuous arcing time is required, the electrode gap may have to be adjusted to maintain the arc.

Ceramic containers, known as combustion boats and used primarily for the analysis of sulfur and carbon in metals, can be purchased from Spectrex or any laboratory-supply house. Small graphite crucibles may also be used as sample containers.

B. Oxyhydrogen solution source

The source shown in Figure B-2 is essentially the same as that used with the Fisher Duo-Spectranal spectroscope for the analysis of solutions (see Chapter 3).

The construction of the electrodes is shown in Figure B-2B. A 3/4-inch length of No. 16 B&S gauge platinum wire *l* is sealed into the end of glass tube *m* and a piece of rosin-core solder *n* is pushed into the tube. Approximately 1 inch of insulation is removed from a 12-inch length of stranded copper wire *o* and the bare end is coated with solder. The glass tube is gently heated in a gas flame until the solder melts and the wire is quickly inserted and held in place until the solder solidifies around it.

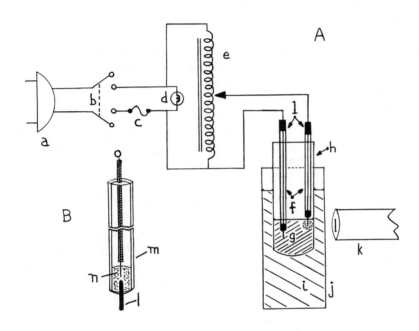

Figure B-2. OXYHYDROGEN ARC SOURCE

A — Source in operation a — plug to a 115-volt a-c outlet; *b —* double-pole, single-throw switch; *c —* 2-ampere fuse; *d —* 115-volt neon indicator light; *e —* autotransformer of 2-ampere capacity or higher; *f —* electrodes; *g —* sample solution; *h —* test tube; *i —* cooling water; *j —* beaker; *k —* spectroscope.
B — Construction of electrodes l — No. 16 B&S gauge platinum wire; *m —* glass tube; *n —* rosin-core solder; *o —* insulated, stranded copper wire.

A support stand is required that will hold the electrodes firmly in place after they have been properly positioned with respect to each other, the surface of sample solution *g*, and spectroscope *k*.

The source is tested with a solution of 1 gram of potassium nitrate in 10 milliliters of concentrated nitric acid diluted with 90 milliliters of distilled water. About 1 inch of test solution is poured into sample tube *h*, electrodes *f* are inserted as shown (if they are too far down, fuse *c* may blow), beaker *j* is filled with cool water *i*, transformer *e* is adjusted to about its midrange, and switch *b* is closed.

A pink glow should appear around the electrode at the surface of the solution indicating that the oxyhydrogen arc is in operation. As the transformer is slowly turned up, the intensity of the arc will increase and soon a crackling noise will be heard. At this point the spectrum should be observed and the voltage increased just enough to give spectrum lines of maximum brightness. The fuse will burn out if too much voltage is applied.

Hydrogen, sodium, and calcium lines should be seen in the spectroscope (the latter two elements are low-level impurities in potassium nitrate) and probably those of platinum and potassium, although platinum lines are largely suppressed and the detection sensitivity of potassium is only 4000 parts per million under these conditions.

The sample-preparation procedures that follow are quoted from the Fisher Duo-Spectranal instruction manual by permission of the Fisher Scientific Company. Tables B-1 and B-2 indicate the concentration levels at which the various elements can be detected.

Preparation of sample material

Known and unknown materials to be excited and analyzed by use of the Duo-Spectranal should be prepared by putting the material to be analyzed into solution. A special solution, known as the nitric acid test solution, is generally used for this purpose. This solution has the following composition:

1 gm	potassium nitrate
10 ml	nitric acid, concentrated, reagent
90 ml	distilled water

The concentrations of the components of this solution should not vary more than plus or minus 10% of their respective amounts. Since not all samples will dissolve directly in this solution, a procedure is given later for preparation of various types of samples.

The potassium nitrate in the test solution tends to enhance the spectral lines of the elements in solution and to suppress the spectral lines of the platinum excitation electrode. Potassium is the only common element which has both the valuable characteristics of greatly suppressing the platinum lines and not producing any lines of its own in the concentration that it is used in the test solution.

The nitric acid is used in the test solution as the preferred electrolyte and also because the nitrates of almost all metallic elements are soluble in dilute nitric acid.

For each analysis performed on the Duo-Spectranal, about 2 milliliters of test solution is used. In general, about 100 milligrams of an unknown should be dissolved in each 2 milliliters of test solution.

Aqua regia when present in traces or in moderate amounts is very damaging to the platinum electrodes. When used for dissolving sample materials, aqua regia should always be completely removed by evaporation to dryness, and the dry residue redissolved in the nitric acid test solution.

The following procedures should be used for dissolving various types of samples.

A. *If the sample material is dry, free from organic matter, and soluble in cold or boiling 10% nitric acid:*

Dissolve, using heat if necessary, approximately 100 milligrams of the sample in approximately 2 milliliters of the nitric acid test solution and analyze the solution directly for the metallic elements using the Duo-Spectranal. If this amount of sample is not available, a smaller amount may be used; however Table B-1 should be consulted regarding the minimum detectable quantity of each element.

B. *If the sample material is dry, free from organic matter, and soluble in cold or boiling aqua regia:*

Dissolve approximately 100 milligrams of the sample in approximately 2 milliliters of aqua regia (one part concentrated nitric acid and three parts concentrated hydrochloric acid), using heat if necessary. After the sample has been completely dissolved, except for silicon dioxide which if present is insoluble, the aqua regia is *completely* removed by evaporating the solution to dryness using an exhaust ventilating hood to remove the corrosive vapors. The dry residue is redissolved in approximately 2 milliliters of the nitric acid test solution and analyzed with the Duo-Spectranal. It is not necessary to filter off any silicon dioxide precipitate.

C. *If the sample material is dry, free from organic matter, and insoluble in cold or boiling aqua regia:*

In some cases, fusion with potassium carbonate is the only method which succeeds in decomposing an insoluble compound. Mix the pulverized sample material with three or four times its bulk of anhydrous potassium carbonate and fuse on a platinum foil. After cooling, dissolve the sample in warm 10% nitric acid. The insoluble gelatinous white precipitate, if any, is silicon dioxide which should be filtered off. Analyze the filtrate by the procedure for the *detection and separation of the elements* described later in this section. If the sample contains a high concentration of silicon dioxide, sufficient sample should be taken to obtain 100 milligrams of dry nonsilicon material for analysis by the Duo-Spectranal.

D. *If the sample material contains water and/or organic material:*

Remove all water and/or organic matter from the sample by evaporation and/or ignition. Take a sufficient amount of sample material to obtain about 100 milligrams of the dry inorganic residue after evaporation or ignition. Smaller amounts of residue may be used if the amount of sample is limited; however Table B-1 should be consulted regarding the minimum detectable quantity of each element. Dissolve the dry inorganic residue in approximately 1 milliliter of aqua regia, using heat if necessary to dissolve the residue completely. Evaporate this aqua regia solution to complete dryness but do not burn the residue. The dry residue is redissolved in approximately 2 milliliters of the nitric acid test solution, using heat if necessary and analyzed with the Duo-Spectranal.

Occasional instances will arise when certain substances may not be suitable for analysis in the nitric acid test solution. For example, tin is not soluble in the nitrate solution. In such cases, a test solution should be used in which the substances will be soluble. In the case of tin, hydrochloric acid and potassium chloride should be substituted for the nitric acid and potassium nitrate.

Frequently, sample materials, whether chemical compounds or alloys, contain high concentrations of one or two metallic elements. In these cases, it is desirable, although not always essential, to separate these preponderant elements by some suitable method so that those metallic elements present in low concentrations may be detected with the Spectranal. In many cases, the following method for the *detection and separation of elements* is very useful for this separation. A sufficient quantity of the sample material should be taken to obtain enough of the low-concentration elements after the separation to be detected by the Duo-Spectranal.

In order to detect traces of metallic elements in aqueous solutions, it is necessary to take a sufficient quantity of the solution and evaporate it to dryness to obtain the metallic elements in sufficient quantity and in concentrated form. Instead of evaporation, the following rapid chemical method for the *detection and separation of elements* is very useful for concentrating traces of many metallic elements in solution.

Detection and separation of groups of
the common metallic elements

This simple precipitation method for detecting the presence or absence of large groups of metallic elements, although not essential for the Duo-Spectranal analysis of elements, has several very useful purposes. This method of detecting and separating groups of metallic elements depends on the solubilities of their sulfides which vary from the two extremes of being either very soluble or very insoluble in acid or alkaline solutions. By using these differences of solubilities of the sulfides, the metallic elements can be easily separated into groups with the same solubility characteristics.

Another purpose of this group method of separation is that it can be used as an approximate semiquantitative method since the amount of sulfide precipitate can be estimated visually as being present in amounts large, medium, small, traces, or entirely absent. The amount of the precipitate will help to decide the amount of sample material which should be used for making a subsequent analysis of the individual elements. The color of the precipitate can also be used as a guide to determine its qualitative composition in some cases. Caution should be used when observing the color of precipitates for analytical purposes, since light-colored precipitates may not be seen when coprecipitated in mixtures with dark-colored precipitates.

Since the sulfides of many metallic elements are extremely insoluble under suitable conditions, this group method of precipitating them may be used as a rapid method for concentrating many metallic elements in dilute solutions. These insoluble metallic sulfides may then be readily redissolved using method B of the preceding section and analyzed in concentrated form by the Duo-Spectranal.

A. Procedure for the Detection and Separation of Groups of the Metallic Elements

Dissolve approximately 1 gram (or less if more is not available) of dry inorganic sample material, or inorganic residue prepared by one of the procedures on page 134, or 135 in approximately 25 milliliters of 10% nitric acid. If the sample is not soluble in 10% nitric acid, it may be dissolved in a small amount of aqua regia (one part concentrated nitric acid and three parts concentrated hydrochloric acid) and then diluted to approximately 25 milliliters with water. To this solution is added about 5 ml of 10% ammonium sulfide solution. This solution is warmed to make the precipitation complete. The ammonium sulfide solution decomposes in acid solution with the formation of a small amount of yellowish colloidal sulfur. This sulfur precipitate should not be confused with metallic sulfide precipitates. Ammonium sulfide solution has a very strong odor and should always be used in a well-ventilated exhaust hood. After the ammonium sulfide addition, make the strongly acid solution slightly but definitely acid by the addition of 10% ammonium hydroxide. The metallic elements in group 1 of Table B-3 all form very insoluble sulfides in this acid solution.

If no precipitate forms, all of the elements in group 1 are absent and need not be analyzed for by the Duo-Spectranal.

If a precipitate does form, filter off and wash it with a few milliliters of warm water. Combine the filtrate and washings. To this solution add 10% ammonium hydroxide until the solution is strongly alkaline. This solution is warmed to make the precipitation complete. The metallic elements in group 2 of Table B-3 all form very insoluble sulfides or hydroxides in this strongly alkaline solution.

If no precipitate forms, all of the elements in group 2 are absent and need not be analyzed for by the Duo-Spectranal.

If a precipitate forms, filter it off, and wash it with a few milliliters of warm water. The filtrate would contain, if present, the elements in group 3 of Table B-3 all of which form sulfides or hydroxides that are soluble in both acid and alkaline aqueous solutions.

Magnesium and calcium are listed in group 3 because their sulfides or hydroxides are soluble in the presence of ammonium nitrate formed in this procedure.

The insoluble metallic sulfides in groups 1 and 2 may be analyzed separately or in combined form by the Duo-Spectranal for the individual elements. Not more than approximately 100 milligrams of the dry precipitate, estimated from the amount of water still present in the wet precipitate, should be used for the analysis. Redissolve the precipitate on the filter paper with a small amount of warm aqua regia. A small amount of sulfur, and silicon dioxide, if present, will remain undissolved on the filter paper. Place this aqua regia filtrate in the excitation chamber tube and evaporate the solution and the drops on the walls of the tube to complete dryness by the gentle application of heat and without burning the insoluble residue. Dissolve the dry residue in approximately 2 milliliters of nitric acid test solution, using heat if necessary. Analyze this solution for the individual metallic elements in Groups 1 and 2 by the Duo-Spectranal.

B. Interfering Metallic Elements

The elements barium, calcium, lithium, sodium, and strontium, all give unusually bright spectral lines, even in low concentrations. These elements interfere with the Duo-Spectranal detection of other elements which produce spectral lines of lower intensities. If, after making a preliminary Duo-Spectranal analysis of a sample for these interfering elements, it is found that one or more of them are present in sufficient concentration to produce their bright lines, they should be removed by taking advantage of the fact that the sulfides of these interfering metallic elements are very soluble in both acid and alkaline solutions as shown in group 3 of Table B-3. The elements cesium, gallium, magnesium, potassium, and rubidium, while not of the interfering type, also have the same sulfide solubility characteristics. These latter elements should be analyzed along with the interfering elements mentioned above in the preliminary Duo-Spectranal analysis of the sample. If the interfering elements are found to be absent or present in only small amounts by the preliminary Duo-Spectranal analysis, the sample material may be analyzed directly for all the other elements by the Duo-Spectranal without the need of separating them into groups by this sulfide precipitation method. If it is necessary to remove one or more of the interfering elements, the above procedure is used.

TABLE B-1

Spectral indentification lines of the common metallic elements
in the oxyhydrogen solution excitation source

Element	Sensitivity in ppm*	Wavelengths in angstrom units.			
		1	2	3	4
Aluminum	15	4663	3961	3944	4842 (bandhead)
Antimony	20	6129	6079	6005	5636
Arsenic	250	5651	5558	5331	5106
Barium	0.5	4554	4934	5535	6142
Bismuth	100	4722	5209	5144	5742
Cadmium	15	5086	4800	4678	6438
Calcium	0. 5	4227	5602	BAND 5565–5470	
Cerium	25	5079	5189	4737	4527
Cesium	4000	4555	4593	6213	——
Chromium	5	5206	4290	4275	4254
Cobalt	50	5369	5352	5281	4121
Copper	25	5218	5105	5153	5782

TABLE B-1 (continued)

Element	Sensitivity in ppm*	Wavelengths in angstrom units			
		1	2	3	4
Gallium	25	4172	4033	——	——
Hydrogen	——	4861	6562	4340	4101
Indium	10	4511	4102	——	——
Iron	10	4404	5326	5270	5230
Lanthanum	25	6296	6249	5379	5302
Lead	150	4060	5609	5370	5005
Lithium	0.5	6103	6708	4603	4972
Magnesium	0.5	5184	5173	5167	4481
Manganese	25	4823	4783	4760	6017
Mercury **	100	5461	4358	5791	5770
Molybdenum	50	5506	5533	5570	6031
Nickel	25	5477	5082	4715	4401
Phosphorus	150	5425	5243	6024	6043
Potassium	4000	4046	5802	6925	——
Silicon	250	5056	5041	6347	6371
Silver	15	5465	5209	——	——
Sodium	Less than 0.5	5896	5890	5675	5670
Strontium	0.5	4607	4215	4078	5481
Tin	25	5799	5589	5563	6453
Titanium	15	5039	5014	4999	4981
Vanadium	50	4421	5698	5705	6086
Yttrium	10	5203	5087	4900	4884
Zinc	5	4810	4722	4680	6362
Zirconium	25	5355	5191	4688	4710

* PPM = parts per million; 1 PPM = 0.0001%.
** Not to be analyzed under fluorescent lights.

TABLE B-2

Spectral identification lines of the semicommon and rare
metallic elements in the oxyhydrogen solution excitation source

Element	Sensitivity in ppm	Wavelengths in angstrom units			
		1	2	3	4
Beryllium	15	4573	4674	5274	——
Dysprosium	50	4212	4046	4195	4187
Erbium	10	5665	5189	4900	4872
Europium	2.5	4662	4627	4594	4435
Gadolinium	20	BAND 6240-5800		——	——
Germanium	400	6021	5178	5133	4815
Gold	200	4812	5230	5837	6278
Hafnium	5	5354	5311	5182	——
Iridium	40	5451	5623	5388	5364
Lanthanum	100	6296	6249	5379	5302
Lutecium	25	5476	6242	6222	6160
Neodymium	25	5293	5115	5090	5249
Niobium	——	5665	4101	4080	4059
Palladium	300	5695	5670	5543	5295
Platinum	750	5477	5369	5059	4552
Praseodymium	50	5381	5300	5270	5111
Rhenium	500	5273	4889	4513	5834
Rhodium	400	6752	5599	5354	4377
Rubidium	4000	4202	4215	6298	6206
Samarium	250	5200	5120	5110	5080
Scandium	5	5527	5081	5031	4247
Tellurium	75	5755	5708	5649	6438
Thallium	5	5350	——	——	——
Thorium	——	5989	5870	4920	6369
Tungsten	——	5072	5053	5805	5735
Ytterbium	40	5481	5539	4935	4786

TABLE B-3

Solubilities and colors of the sulfides of the metallic elements

Common elements	Solubility of sulfide in		Color of insoluble sulfide
	Acid solution	Alkaline solution	

GROUP 1

Common elements	Acid solution	Alkaline solution	Color of insoluble sulfide
Bismuth	I	I	Black
Cobalt	I	I	Black
Copper	I	I	Black
Gold	I	I	Black
Iridium	I	I	Black
Lead	I	I	Black
Mercury	I	I	Black
Nickel	I	I	Black
Palladium	I	I	Black
Silver	I	I	Black
Tellurium	I	I	Black
Columbium	I	I	White
Germanium	I	S	White
Tantalum	I	I	White
Tungsten	I	S	White
Arsenic	I	S	Yellow
Cadmium	I	S	Yellow
Selenium	I	S	Yellow
Tin	I	I	Yellow
Antimony	I	I	Orange
Molybdenum	I	I	Blue
Platinum	I	I	Gray
Rhodium	I	I	Brown

TABLE B-3 (continued)

Common elements	Solubility of sulfide in		Color of insoluble sulfide
	Acid solution	Alkaline solution	

GROUP 2

Aluminum	S	I	White
Beryllium	S	I	White
Cerium	S	I	White
Indium	S	I	White
Titanium	S	I	White
Zinc	S	I	White
Chromium	S	I	Bluish
Iron	S	I	Black
Manganese	S	I	Pink
Thallium	S	I	Black
Vanadium	S	I	Brown
Zirconium	S	I	Green

GROUP 3

Barium	S	S	——
Calcium	S	S	——
Cesium	S	S	——
Gallium	S	S	——
Lithium	S	S	——
Magnesium	S	S	——
Potassium	S	S	——
Rubidium	S	S	——
Sodium	S	S	——
Strontium	S	S	——

I denotes insoluble. S denotes soluble. The sulfides of some of these elements hydrolyze instantly in aqueous solutions to their corresponding hydroxides whose solubilities and colors are shown in the table instead of those of their unstable sulfides.

The design and construction of a spectrum-line identification system

A *master film* is a film strip with a wavelength scale, an iron reference spectrum, and a *master spectrum,* i.e., a simulated spectrogram composed of the most-sensitive lines of the elements.

A section of a master film is seen on the screen of the film viewer-comparator in Figure 3-15 below the corresponding wavelength region of four sample spectra. The black dots and chemical symbols identify the lines in the master spectrum and the numbers belong to the wavelength scale. A master film can be used only with spectra whose dispersion it matches.

The design and construction of a line-identification system that requires only a simple overhead projector or a 35-millimeter slide projector in place of an expensive film viewer-comparator is described in the following.

An overhead projector must be provided with a guide through which the sample film can be pulled as it is examined. If a slide projector is used, it must be of the single-slide type, such as the Bausch & Lomb Balmite 50, that allows horizontal passage of the film.

The information on a master film is inscribed on cards that are mounted on the projection screen just below the image of the sample-film spectra. A master-line identification system for a spectrograph whose linear dispersion and wavelength range are, for example, 0.0625 millimeter/A and 5000 A (2200-7200 A), respectively, can be designed as follows.

The width of the picture in a 35-millimeter slide is equal to the length of a 560 A section of the spectrogram (35/0.0625 = 560). In other words, 560 angstroms can be viewed at a time with a slide projector. If the film guide on the table of an overhead projector is provided with a 35-millimeter mask, the same figures will apply.

For convenience, let us work with 500 angstroms rather than 560 and choose a projector-to-screen distance that magnifies the spectrum ten times. Then, 500 angstroms will occupy 31.25 centimeters on the screen ($35 \times 500 / 560 = 31.25$), with an apparent linear dispersion of 0.625 millimeters/A.

If the spectrum is divided into 1100-angstrom sections with 100 angstroms of overlap, the wavelength range covered by each section will be as given in Table C-1.

TABLE C-1

Wavelength Range for Each Section of the Spectrum

Section	Wavelength range in angstroms
A	2200-3300
B	3200-4300
C	4200-5300
D	5200-6300
E	6200-7200

For each section, the applicable part of the master spectrum, wavelength scale, and iron reference spectrum are inscribed on a strip of heavy white cardboard (30×6 inches) as shown in Figure C-1 on *b* which represents a part of the card for section B. Wavelength scale *IV* is laid out to match the linear dispersion of the projected sample spectrum, i.e., 0.625 millimeter/A. Lines for iron reference spectrum *III* are selected from the M.I.T. wavelength tables or any other reasonably complete wavelength tables such as those in *Chemical Spectroscopy* by Brode or the *Handbook of Chemistry and Physics* (see the references for Chapter 4). The strongest lines are chosen to give a density of roughly one line per 10 angstroms. The wavelengths of the lines shown in iron reference spectrum *III* are 3239.4, 3251.2, 3265.6, 3271.0, and 3280.3 A.

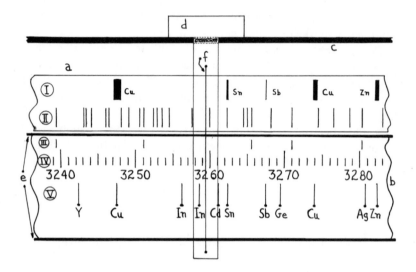

Figure C-1. THE SAMPLE-FILM IMAGE AND MASTER-SPECTRUM CARD
ON THE PROJECTION SCREEN
a — projected sample-film section; *b* — master card made of white cardboard; *c* —
T-square guide; *d* — transparent plastic T-square; *e* — cardboard guides; *f* — reference
line on T-square; I — sample spectrogram; II — iron spectrum; III — iron reference
lines; IV — wavelength scale; V — master spectrum (3240 to 3280 A segment of
wavelength section B; see Table C-1).

The lines in master spectrum *V* are chosen from those listed in
Table 4-1. The master spectrum should include the carbon 2478.6 line
and indicate the location of the cyanogen bandheads as these are useful
reference points.

The projected image of the 3240 to 3280 A region of sample spectrogram *a* is shown as it would appear on the screen above and aligned with
master card *b*. The lines in spectrum *I* are directly above the corresponding ones in master spectrum *V,* and each line in iron reference spectrum *III*
is directly below the corresponding line in spectrum *II.*

The projection screen should be a solid surface, such as a wall, so that
guides *e* for the spectrum cards and guide *c* for T-square *d* can be attached to it.

Before a film is projected, it should be marked near the top or bottom
edge with wavelength identifying symbols at approximately 2450, 2950,
3450, 3950, 4450, 4950, 5450, 5950, 6450, and 6950 A. These points
can be easily located with a ruler. One of the symbols will always be on
the screen to indicate the region of the spectrum that is being viewed.

The master cards should be bordered on their horizontal edges with thin 1/4-inch-wide strips of wood that slide smoothly inside guides *e*. These strips will prolong the life of the cards. Transparent plastic T-square *d* slides along guide *c* so that reference line *f* can be moved to any point on the screen.

To view a film, the desired wavelength region is projected and the appropriate master card is pushed into guides *e*. The wavelength identifying symbol on the film is lined up approximately with its corresponding number on scale *IV* and then, with the help of reference line *f*, master card *b* is moved into exact alignment with the sample film.

This can be done by bringing reference iron spectra *II* and *III* into coincidence or aligning a known line in spectrum *I* with the corresponding line in spectrum *V* or wavelength scale *IV*. Reference line *f* can now be used to measure the wavelength of any line on the screen in sample spectrum *I*, or to check it for coincidence with a line in master spectrum *V*. These operations can be performed reliably only if the projector has been positioned to give a spectral dispersion of 0.625 millimeters/A. The image dispersion is adjusted by projecting a familiar spectrogram and measuring the distance between two known lines. After the projector has been positioned for a magnification factor of 10, it must be clamped in place so that it cannot be moved accidentally.

Spectrum *I* in Figure C-1 shows the lines in the 3240 to 3280 A region that would be of interest for the analysis of a 70/30 yellow-brass sample. The relative widths of the lines indicate that copper and zinc are the major constituents, tin a minor element, and antimony an impurity.

Since, as discussed in Chapter 2, spectral dispersion varies somewhat with wavelength, the master-spectrum cards can be made even more exact by determining, on a known spectrogram, the dispersion of each wavelength section (see Table C-1) separately rather than using the average dispersion of the entire spectrum. Each card is then made up on the basis of the dispersion figure that applies to its wavelength region.

Wavelength conversion factors

1 angstrom $= 10^{-10}$ meters
1 angstrom $= 10^{-8}$ centimeters
1 angstrom $= 10^{-4}$ microns
1 micron $= 10^{-4}$ centimeters
1 millimicron $= 10^{-3}$ microns
1 millimicron $= 10$ angstroms

GLOSSARY

ANALYTICAL LINE — A spectral line used for measuring element concentration.

ANGSTROM (A) (10^{-8} centimeter) — A unit used for measuring the length of light waves.

ASTIGMATISM — The inability of a lens or concave mirror to focus the vertical and horizontal components of off-axis rays in the same plane.

COLLIMATOR — A lens or mirror that converts diverging light to parallel light.

CONTINUOUS SPECTRUM — A spectrum that includes all wavelengths between its wavelength limits.

COUNTERELECTRODE — The electrode used with the sample-containing electrode to form an electric arc.

DETECTION LIMIT — The smallest amount of an element that can be detected by spectroscopic analysis.

DIFFRACTION — The change in direction of light and its modification as it passes by the edge of an opaque object or through a small opening, or when it passes through or is reflected from a closely ruled surface.

DIFFRACTION GRATING — A spectrum-producing device consisting of a surface ruled with many fine, closely spaced, equidistant, parallel grooves.

DISPERSION — The separation of light into its component wavelengths.

EMISSION SPECTRUM — A spectrum due to light emitted by atoms or molecules.

EMULSION CALIBRATION CURVE — A graph that shows the relationship between the image density on a photographic emulsion and the intensity of the light producing the image.

EXCITATION POTENTIAL — The energy, in electron volts, required to excite an atom to emit a given wavelength of light.

EXCITATION SOURCE — An energy source that stimulates matter to emit light.

146

FRAUNHOFER LINES — Dark lines superimposed on the sun's continuous spectrum.

GHOST LINES — False lines in a spectrum due to diffraction-grating imperfections.

HOMOLOGOUS LINES — A pair of analytical and internal standard lines used for the quantitative analysis of an element.

INDEX OF REFRACTION — The ratio of the velocities of light of a given wavelength in two different media.

INDEX POINT — The point on a working curve at which the element-concentration value corresponds to unity intensity ratio of the analytical and internal standard lines.

INFRARED RADIATION — An invisible radiation whose wavelength is greater than that of visible red light.

INTENSITY RATIO — The ratio of the intensities of the analytical and internal standard lines of a homologous pair.

INTERFERENCE — The coincidence of crests, and crests and troughs, of light waves to produce alternating light and dark bands.

INTERFERENCE (LINE) — The overlapping of spectral lines that cannot be separated by a spectroscope or spectrograph because of insufficient resolving power.

INTERNAL STANDARD LINE — A spectral line whose intensity is compared with that of an analytical line.

LINE SPECTRUM — A spectrum composed of discrete wavelengths (as opposed to a continuous spectrum).

LINEAR DISPERSION — The separation of wavelengths in a spectrum in terms of linear distance (usually expressed as millimeters per angstrom).

LOGARITHMIC SECTOR — A disc, with a perimeter shaped like a logarithmic spiral, that controls the amount of light entering a spectrograph during a quantitative analysis.

MATRIX — The major chemical components of a substance.

MEDIUM — Matter through which light passes.

MILLIMICRON (10^{-4} centimeter) — A unit used to express the wavelength of light.

MINIMUM DEVIATION — The smallest possible angle of deviation of a light ray as it passes through a prism.

MOLECULAR BAND — A series of lines emitted by a molecule.

MONOCHROMATIC LIGHT — Light of a single wavelength.

PERSISTENT LINE — A spectral line that is visible at or near the detection limit of an element.

PRISM — A piece of glass (or other transparent material) with a triangular cross section used for producing a spectrum.

RECIPROCAL LINEAR DISPERSION — The inverse of linear dispersion.

REFRACTION — The change in the direction of light as it passes from one medium into another of different density.

RESOLVING POWER — The ability of a spectroscope or spectrograph to present closely adjacent wavelengths as separate lines.

ROWLAND CIRCLE — A circle on which are located the slit, grating, and camera of a concave-diffraction-grating spectrograph.

SAMPLE ELECTRODE — The electrode that holds the sample being analyzed.

SELF-ABSORPTION — Absorption by a substance of light of a wavelength that it can emit.

SELF-REVERSAL — Extreme self-absorption that results in changing of the image of a spectral line from its normal color to black.

SENSITIVE LINE — The same as persistent line.

SLIT — A narrow rectangular opening through which light enters a spectroscope.

SPECTRAL LINE — An image of the spectroscope slit produced by light of a specific wavelength.

SPECTRAL ORDERS — Multiple spectra with increasing dispersion formed by a diffraction grating.

SPECTROGRAM — A photograph of a spectrum.

SPECTROGRAPH — An instrument for producing spectra and recording them on a film or plate.

SPECTROMETER — An optical instrument with an entrance slit, a dispersing device, and one or more exit slits each of which receives light of a specific wavelength within the spectral range of the instrument.

SPECTROSCOPE — An instrument for producing and viewing spectra.

SPECTROSCOPY — (1) The study of spectral theory and the interaction between radiation and matter; (2) the use of the spectroscope.

SPECTRUM — The ordered array of wavelengths that is produced when light is dispersed by a prism or a diffraction grating.

STEP SECTOR — A disc with a series of steps cut in its perimeter that is used to calibrate the photographic emulsion of a spectrograph.

STIGMATISM — The ability of an optical system to focus both horizontal and vertical components of off-axis rays in the same plane.

ULTRAVIOLET RADIATION — An invisible radiation of a wavelength shorter than that of visible violet light.

VARIABLE-APERTURE SECTOR — A disc with openings of variable size which is used to control the amount of light that enters a spectrograph and prevent overexposure of the spectrogram.

WAVELENGTH — The linear distance between corresponding points of adjacent light waves.

WORKING CURVE — A graph that shows the relationship between element concentration and the intensity ratio of the analytical and internal standard lines.

Atomic weights of the chemical elements

Element	Symbol	Atomic weight	Element	Symbol	Atomic weight
Aluminum	Al	26.98	Molybdenum	Mo	95.94
Antimony	Sb	121.75	Neodymium	Nd	144.24
Arsenic	As	74.92	Nickel	Ni	58.71
Barium	Ba	137.34	Niobium	Nb	92.91
Beryllium	Be	9.01	Nitrogen	N	14.01
Bismuth	Bi	208.98	Osmium	Os	190.20
Boron	B	10.81	Oxygen	O	16.00
Bromine	Br	79.91	Palladium	Pd	106.40
Cadmium	Cd	112.40	Phosphorus	P	30.97
Calcium	Ca	40.08	Platinum	Pt	195.09
Carbon	C	12.01	Potassium	K	39.10
Cerium	Ce	140.12	Praseodymium	Pr	140.91
Cesium	Cs	132.91	Rhenium	Re	186.23
Chlorine	Cl	35.45	Rhodium	Rh	102.91
Chromium	Cr	52.00	Rubidium	Rb	85.47
Cobalt	Co	58.93	Ruthenium	Ru	101.07
Copper	Cu	63.54	Samarium	Sm	150.35
Dysprosium	Dy	162.50	Scandium	Sc	44.96
Erbium	Er	167.26	Selenium	Se	78.96
Europium	Eu	151.96	Silicon	Si	28.09
Fluorine	F	19.00	Silver	Ag	107.87
Gadolinium	Gd	157.25	Sodium	Na	22.99
Gallium	Ga	69.72	Strontium	Sr	87.62
Germanium	Ge	72.59	Sulfur	S	32.06
Gold	Au	196.97	Tantalum	Ta	180.95
Hafnium	Hf	178.49	Tellurium	Te	127.60
Holmium	Ho	164.93	Terbium	Tb	158.92
Hydrogen	H	1.01	Thallium	Tl	204.37
Indium	In	114.82	Thorium	Th	232.04
Iodine	I	126.90	Thulium	Tm	168.93
Iridium	Ir	192.20	Tin	Sn	118.69
Iron	Fe	55.85	Titanium	Ti	47.90
Lanthanum	La	138.91	Tungsten	W	183.85
Lead	Pb	207.19	Uranium	U	238.03
Lithium	Li	6.94	Vanadium	V	50.94
Lutecium	Lu	174.97	Ytterbium	Yb	173.04
Magnesium	Mg	24.31	Yttrium	Y	88.91
Manganese	Mn	54.94	Zinc	Zn	65.37
Mercury	Hg	200.59	Zirconium	Zr	91.22

Sources of spectrochemical accessories, components, and supplies

Diffraction gratings and gas spectrum tubes

Central Scientific Co.
2600 So. Kostner Ave.
Chicago, Ill. 60623

Edmund Scientific Co.
150 Edscorp Building
Barrington, N. J. 08807

Electrodes and other graphite products

Spectrex Corp.
3594 Haven Ave.
Redwood City, Ca. 94063
(cored electrodes for 115 volt a-c arc)

Ultra Carbon Corp.
1310 No. Madison St.
P.O. Box 747
Bay City, Mich. 48706

Optical components (lenses, prisms, etc.)

Ealing Corp.
2225 Massachusetts Ave.
Cambridge, Mass. 02140

Edmund Scientific Co.
150 Edscorp Building
Barrington, N. J. 08807

Esco Products
171 Oak Ridge Road
Oak Ridge, N. J. 07438
(quartz lenses and prisms)

Optical Industries, Inc.
1218 E. Pomona St.
Santa Ana, Ca. 92707

Operating supplies (photographic, electrodes, etc.), accessories, sample-preparation equipment, and reference standards

Angstrom, Inc.
P.O. Box 248
Belleville, Mich. 48111

Applied Research Laboratories
P.O. Box 129
Sunland, Ca. 91040

Baird-Atomic, Inc.
125 Middlesex Turnpike
Bedford, Mass. 01730

Harry W. Dietert Co.
9330 Roselawn Ave.
Detroit, Mich. 48204
(molds for casting metal samples)

Jarrell-Ash Div.,
Fisher Scientific Co.
590 Lincoln St.
Waltham, Mass. 02154

National Spectrographic Labs.
19500 So. Miles Road
Cleveland, Ohio 44128

Spex Industries
3880 Park Ave.
Metuchen, N. J. 08840

Central Scientific Co.
2600 So. Kostner Ave.
Chicago, Ill. 60623
(spectroscopes; electrode holders, logarithmic sector discs, and other optical-bench accessories)

Index